FANTASY POSTCARDS

With Price Guide

A Comprehensive Reference

J. L. Mashburn

COLONIAL HOUSE PUBLISHERS
ENKA, NORTH CAROLINA 28728 USA

Publisher: J. L. Mashburn
Editor: Emma Mashburn

Cover and Interior Design: Picture Perfect Publishing, Inc.
Electronic Page Assembly: Picture Perfect Publishing, Inc.

A Colonial House Production

Printed in the United States of America

First Edition

10 9 8 7 6 5 4 3 2 1

Library of Congress Cataloging-in-Publication

Mashburn, J. L. (Joseph Lee)
      Fantasy Postcards with price guide : a comprehensive reference / J. L. Mashburn
          p. cm.
      Includes index.
      ISBN 1-885940-02-5
      1. Postcards--Collectors and collecting--Catalogs. 2. Postcards--History--20th century--Catalogs. 3. Fantasy in art--Catalogs.
      I. Title.
      NC1878.F26M37 1996
      741.6'83--dc20   96-9617
                                            CIP

AN IMPORTANT NOTICE TO
THE READERS OF THIS PRICE GUIDE:

The comprehensive nature of compiling data and prices on the thousands of cards, sets and series that this publication represents gives many probabilities for error. Although all information has been compiled from reliable sources, experienced collectors and dealers, some data may still be questionable. The author and publisher will not be held responsible for any losses that might occur in the purchase or sale of cards because of the information contained herein. The final values should be an agreement between the buyer and seller.

The author will be most pleased to receive notice of errors so that they may be corrected in future editions. Contact: J. L. Mashburn, Colonial House, Box 609, Enka, NC 28728.

This book and other Mashburn price guides are available worldwide on the Internet at Colonial House Website: http://www.postcard-books.com

CONTENTS

DEDICATION

To our four beloved grand-
children -- Jessica, Alexandra,
Nicholas and Elizabeth -- we
dedicate this book.

The majority of the chapters --
Fairies, Fairy Tales & Nursery
Rhymes, Dressed Animals,
Mermaids, Teddy Bears, Santas,
and the whimsical topics in
the miscellaneous section --
are reminders of the sweetness
and innocence of our childhood.

We hope all of you will enjoy
this publication as much as we
have enjoyed preparing it for you.

ACKNOWLEDGMENTS

Many individuals have made valuable contributions to this publication. Although it is impossible to list everyone, the following have given unselfishly of their time, their expertise, and their concerted effort to make this book as complete and interesting as possible.

Special thanks to **John and Sandy Millns** for their tremendous support in supplying innumerable checklists plus hundreds of wonderful postcards for use in scanning. Their suggestions and vital information relating to cards of the lovable Dressed Animals, the Fairies and Fairy Tales, Hold-To-Lights, Santas and others were really a factor in making this book a reality.

Special thanks again to **Shirley** and **Dale Hendricks** who continue to help whenever I call. They allowed us to scan many of the wonderful Louis Wain cats and dogs, the rare S. L. Schmucker Detroit fantasy groups, and many great Santa cards from their personal collections. They have always been great supporters in the production of our books, and collectors have benefited greatly from their generosity.

Our sincere thanks also to **Marilyn Brust** for allowing us to scan Teddy Bears from her fabulous collection, to **Alyce Thorson** for continuing to supply us with new artists and checklists, to **Carla Zemke, Pat Eicher, Elaine Taylor, George Parola,** and **Dr. Dennis Hart** for their most welcomed contributions in supplying additions to checklists, cards for scanning, and other select information as needed.

Special thanks go also to **Martin Shapiro, Fred Kahn, Andreas Brown, George Gibbs,** and **Michael Leach** for their tremendous support and help in so many ways. As always, and most of all, I wish to thank my wife **Emma** for making it all possible.

I want to thank all the postcard dealers who helped so tremendously at shows we attended in Orlando, Milwaukee, Nashville and New York this year. It was very exciting to meet new and old acquaintances and to share some time with them. So many went out of their way to find cards for us, offer advice, and supply information and values on cards we needed for this book. Postcard people, as I have always contended, have to be the nicest people in the world!

Reproduction of Postcards in this Book

All images in this edition are the final results of using a computer program to scan each card. It is then photostyled to the best grayscale clarity before placing it in the text. Real photo and black and white cards are best for this process, and images reproduce very well. However, since the majority of original postcards were printed in so many colors and shades it is sometimes difficult to reproduce them in black and white. This is especially true for some of the lighter pastel colored Fairies, Fairy Tales, Wagner, and color nudes with shadowed areas that are hard to reproduce. Cards appearing on the cover, which are reproduced in their beautiful colors, are also shown in black and white in various sections of the book.

The card shown above, an image of a lovely child by Irene Marcellus, has outstanding, vivid colors. Observing these beautiful and radiant colors is a major part of the joy and magic in collecting postcards.

Chapter 1

Introduction

Fantasy, according to **Webster**, means imagination or fancy; wild visionary fancy; an odd notion or whim; an unnatural or bizarre mental image in one's mind; a highly imaginative poem or play. Fantasy touches everyone...from little children with wonderful visions of fairyland and fairy tales to the old man dreaming of days gone by. If the readers of this book will take the time to observe, all of these definitions can come to life on beautiful and wonderful fantasy postcards!

It has been estimated that of all artist-drawn postcards issued from 1900 to 1930, over 30 percent had a fantasy theme. With all the huge quantities of these common and rare marvels of the fanciful, the exotic and the grotesque, it is no wonder that these wonderful postcards have become so intriguing to collectors worldwide. Their high availability and great variety of motifs are among the reasons for their popularity.

The most delightful fantasy issues were those printed by the great German printers who were so advanced in the trade that publishers from all over the world commissioned them for their printing needs. They were well known for their fantasy-in-print concepts, and exported millions of wonderful cards. Included were many of their own German-artist stock designs, but with captions in the language of the importing nations. It is for this reason that so many cards with the same image turn up with different wording or slight variations. The French were also great printers, and are well known for the great clarity and high quality of their photographic works. This is especially true of their fantasy photo montage issues.

On a somewhat negative side, Fantasy is an illusion. It can be an unreal, deceptive, or misleading appearance or image of false perception or interpretation of what one sees. Fantasy is a frame of mind. It all depends on whether happenings have triggered happy states or negative ones. Many of these illusionary traits are very apparent in Death Fantasy and other bizarre themes such as those seen in the works of artist S. Schneider, as well as those portraying Salome and the severed head of John the Baptist.

In a broader perspective, a great proportion of all Fantasy postcards were drawn and issued solely for the enjoyment of children. The beautiful fairies, the exciting fairy tales, the learning tools of nursery rhymes, the wonderful dressed animals...and even Halloween and Santa...were a part of the happy, learning experience in the early lives of most all children. It is no wonder that today's collector is so enthralled with this material, for it brings back fanciful memories from their own childhood.

Good fantasy cards have not always been as plentiful as they are today, and many U.S. collectors are just now being introduced to this wonderful field. It is true that there were many fantasy cards issued for the American market, but while they were quite good they were also very limited. Before the influx of foreign cards to the U.S. in the late 70's and 80's, collectors had to be content with Halloweens, Santas, a few nursery rhymes and fairy tales, the works of Dwig, S. L. Schmucker and a handful of other artists...not really enough to have a fantasy category.

As U.S. collectors and dealers began postcard buying expeditions to England and all the countries of Europe, more of the fabulous fantasy cards began appearing in auctions and at shows in dealer stocks. The quality of these cards, especially the early chromolithographs, made a deep impression on those who had not previously been exposed to them.

The rest, of course, is now history as everyone has now discovered them. No longer are German, French, Italian, or other cards with their foreign language caption deemed "foreign" cards. Collectors are only concerned, as they truly should be, that they are of the motif they collect, and if they contain the beauty and eye appeal that they desire for their collection.

While prices are relatively high for many fantasy cards, there are still many quality images that are grossly under-priced and waiting for those who have a desire for cards of the fantasy world!

BRIEF HISTORY OF THE U.S. POSTCARD

On May 1, 1893, the first American picture postcards were sold or distributed at the World's Colombian Exposition in Chicago. They became extremely popular and widely acclaimed as hundreds of thousands were sold to visitors at the gala event. From this fantastic beginning the future of the picture postcard was assured, and it was soon to become one of the country's leading industries.

These postcards, now over 100 years old, pictured beautiful and colorful views of the Exposition buildings and displays, as well as products of countries and manufacturers throughout the world. Other cards were also issued to advertise the Exposition itself, and were used by visitors to mail or take back home as proof of their attendance at the event. The beauty of the cards, their small size and low cost, made them a great delight for collectors and gift givers.

Fuelled by the great results of this triumphant beginning for postcards, manufacturers and merchants started using them to advertise their products and services. The cards were either distributed by salesmen or sent by mail to other manufacturers or merchants. Officials of large cities and tourist resorts, believing in the adage that "a picture is worth a thousand words," commissioned publishers to print multi-view cards of interesting sites in their cities. These soon became single views of all the important buildings and street scenes and points of interest. Big publishers, taking advantage of the new craze, dispatched hordes of photographers to all the big cities and resort areas to take pictures of everything of interest.

The artist and magazine illustrator, heretofore limited to sales of portraits, prints, magazine articles and covers, welcomed the new medium and soon became major contributors. Glamour artists Harrison Fisher, Philip Boileau, the Christys, Charles Dana Gibson, Clarence Underwood and others became household names, and the postcard helped them gain worldwide acclaim.

The collecting of postcards became one of the leading hobbies, not only in the U.S. but throughout the world. Large albums served as a convenient means of displaying and protecting the cards, and almost everyone had one or more in which to store their treasured mementos. This collecting craze era, known as "Postcard's Golden Years," waned and virtually terminated in the 1914-1918 era of World War I. A postcard tariff, imposed by the United States, and intervention of Germany (where almost all were printed for the U.S. Trade) into the war brought an end to the fabulous era.

Many new firms in the U.S. began publishing cards in 1915; however, their printing technology was very poor compared to that used in Germany. Reproduction of old views and images, and the resulting poor quality finally sealed the doom for the postcard publisher and collector. With no new treasures to add to collections, the big albums were removed from their familiar station in the living or viewing rooms and placed in the attic or basement trunks. Later generations, with little interest in the hobbies of their ancestors, disposed of many of these beautiful works of art. However, many millions were saved and remain today for the enjoyment of the collector. They also provide excellent material for historians.

HISTORY RECORDED ON POSTCARDS

The events of history, beginning in the early 1890's, are recorded on postcards. The era of the event can be dated in several different ways. The first, and most factual, is the postmark date providing that the cards were postally used. The second is the knowledge of knowing when a particular type card was published ... whether it was a (1) Pioneer issue, (2) Private Mailing Card, (3) Undivided Back, (4) Divided Back, (5) White Border, (6) Linen, or (7) Chrome.

Knowing the name of the publisher and when he was in business, as well as his numbering system, can also be a tremendous help in dating a card. For Real Photo cards, the process used is normally shown on the back. The means to identify the age and Postcard Eras can be found later in this chapter.

HOW TO USE THIS PRICE GUIDE

This price guide has been uniquely designed to serve the needs of both the beginning and advanced collector, as well as the established postcard dealer. Our attempt to provide a comprehensive guide to fantasy postcards dating from the 1900's through the 1940's makes it possible for even the novice collector to consult it with confidence and ease in finding each particular listing. The following important explanations summarize the general practices that will help in getting the most benefits from its use.

CATEGORICAL ARRANGEMENT

Cards are arranged by category, and each category is listed in the Table of Contents. In the Artist-Signed categories, cards that were drawn or painted are listed in two different sections -- either signed or unsigned. Artists are always listed alphabetically, with the name of their publisher, series number if applicable, and the caption from each card, if any.

The Publishers section of each category includes all cards that had a publisher byline but did not include an artist's signature on the picture side. Publishers are also listed alphabetically. If a series name or number was included, this information was placed on the following line. The card number and the card caption, if any, and the value in VG (Very Good) and EX (Excellent) conditions are printed on the third line. If further card captions, in a set or series, are available these are printed below the first caption, and so on.

Anonymous cards or sets are listed in some instances. An anonymous listing has no artist signature, publisher byline, or other means, except the image, to identify it. However, it may have a card number (usually a series number). These numbers are listed as a means of possible identification when no other is available.

LISTINGS

Listings may be identified as follows:

1. **SECTION** (Fairies, Santas, etc.)
2. **ARTIST** (Listed in Bold Capital Letters) when available.
3. **PUBLISHER** (Listed in Bold, either all caps or lower case).
4. **NAME OF SERIES; OR SERIES NUMBER.**
5. **NUMBER OF CARDS IN SET OR SERIES** (Enclosed in Parentheses) when available.
6. **CARD NUMBER**, if any.
7. **CAPTION OR TITLE OF CARD** (Enclosed in Quotation Marks).
8. **PRICE OF 1 CARD IN VERY GOOD CONDITION AND PRICE OF 1 CARD IN EXCELLENT CONDITION.**

Example of above for Artist-Signed Listing:

1. **Artist has first listing under each heading**
2. **FRANCES BRUNDAGE**
3. **Raphael Tuck & Sons**
4. **Series** 4095 "Little Sunbeams"
5. (3)
6. "Little Bo Peep"
7. $35 - 40 and $40 - 45

Example of a publisher listing:

1. **Publisher listed first when no artist is listed**
2. **P.F.B. (Paul Finkenrath, Berlin)**
3. **Series 3714**
4. **Fairy Tales** (not listed as such)
5. **(6)**　6 cards in series
6. **"Cinderella"**
7. $25 - 30 and $30 - 35

ABBREVIATIONS USED IN THIS BOOK

(B&W)	Black and White
(Emb.)	Embossed or Raised Printing
G.B.	Great Britain
VG	Very Good (condition)
EX	Excellent (condition)
(PMC)	Private Mailing Cards
(R.P.)	Real Photo Type
(UndB)	Undivided Backs
(Uns.)	Unsigned
U.S.	United States
K.	Krampus

CONDITION AND GRADING OF POSTCARDS

The condition of a postcard, as with old coins, stamps, books, etc., is an extremely important factor in pricing it for the collector, the dealer, and for those having found cards to sell. Damaged, worn, creased, or dirty cards — cards in less than Very Good condition— are almost uncollectible unless they are to be used as a space filler until a better one is found. Collectors should never buy a damaged card if they expect to sell it later on; however, the rarity of a card may make any condition acceptable.

It is necessary that some sort of card grading standard be used so that buyer and seller may come to an informed agreement on the value of a card. Two different collectible conditions, **Very Good** and **Excellent,** are used in the **FANTASY POSTCARDS, With Price Guide** book. There are, of course, higher and lower grades, but these two will be most normally seen and most normally quoted for postcards sold throughout the hobby.

The standard grading system adapted by most dealers and by the leading postcard hobby publications in the field, *Barr's Post Card News* and *Post Card Collector,* is listed below with their permission:

M—MINT. A perfect card just as it comes from the printing press. No marks, bends, or creases. No writing or postmarks. A clean and fresh card. Seldom seen.

NM—NEAR MINT. Like Mint but very light aging or very slight discoloration from being in an album for many years. Not as sharp or crisp.

EX—EXCELLENT. Like mint in appearance with no bends or creases, or rounded or blunt corners. May be postally used or unused and with writing and postmark only on the address side. A clean, fresh card on the picture side.

VG—VERY GOOD. Corners may be just a bit blunt or rounded. Almost undetectable crease or bend that does not detract from overall appearance of the picture side. May have writing or postal cancellation on address side. A very collectible card.

G—GOOD. Corners may be noticeably blunt or rounded with noticeably slight bends or creases. May be postally used or have writing on address side. Less than VG.

FR—FAIR. Card is intact. Excess soil, stains, creases, writing, or cancellation may affect picture. Could be a scarce card that is difficult to find in any condition.

Postcard dealers always want better condition cards that have no defects. Collectors should keep this in mind if they have cards to sell. Therefore, anyone building a collection should maintain a standard for condition and stick to it. Even if the asking price is a little higher when a card is purchased, it will be worth the cost when it is resold.

VALUATIONS

The postcard values quoted in this publication represent the current retail market. They were compiled with the assistance of some of the leading dealers and collectors in the U.S., dealer pricing at shows, personal dealer communications, from the author's personal purchasing worldwide, from his approval sales, and from his active day-to-day involvement in the postcard field.

Some values were also compiled from observations of listings in auctions, auction catalogs (U.S., Europe, and Great Britain), prices realized and fixed price sales in the fine hobby publications, *Barr's Post Card News* and *Postcard Collector*, and other related publications.

It must be stressed that this price guide and reference work is intended to serve only as an aid in evaluating postcards. It should not be used otherwise. As we all know, actual market conditions change constantly, and prices may fluctuate. The trend for postcards, especially the better material, continues to be to the upside.

Publication of this price guide is not intended to be a solicitation to buy or sell any of the cards listed.

Price ranges for cards in both **Very Good** and **Excellent** conditions are found at the end of each listing. Prices for cards in less than Very Good condition would be much lower, while those grading above Excellent might command relatively higher prices.

Without exception, prices quoted are for **one** card, whether it be a single entity or one card in a complete set or series. Note that after many entries a number is enclosed in parentheses; e.g., (6). This number indicates the total number of cards in a set or in a series. The price listed is for one card in the set and must be multiplied by this number to determine the value of a complete set.

WHY PRICE RANGES ARE QUOTED

For cards graded both **Very Good** and **Excellent**, price ranges are quoted for four major reasons. Any one, or more, of the following can determine the difference in the high or low prices in each of the listing ranges.

1. Prices vary in different geographical areas across the U.S. At this time, they continue to be somewhat higher on the Pacific coast and other western states. They tend to be a little lower in the East and somewhere in-between in the central and Midwestern states. For instance, a card with a price range of $6.00-8.00 might sell for $6.00 in the East, $7.00 in the Mid-West and $8.00 in the Far West.

2. Dealer price valuations also vary. Those who continually set up at postcard shows seem to have a better feel for prices and know

which cards are selling well and, therefore, can adjust their prices accordingly. Dealers who sell only by mail, or by mail auction, tend to price their cards (or list estimated values in their auctions) just a bit higher. They usually are able to realize these prices because of a wider collector market base obtained by the large number of subscribers served by the nationally distributed postcard auction publications. The publications also reach collectors who are unable to attend shows and are, therefore, willing to pay a little more to win that particular lot.

3.   Cards that have been sent on approvals quite often are priced higher than at postcard shows, etc., because the dealer has spent more time in selecting and handling. He is usually working from a customer "want list."

4.   Cards that are in great demand, or "hot" topics, also have wider price ranges. As collector interests rise there is a greater disparity in values because of supply and demand.

5.   Card appearance and the subject in a set or series can also cause a variance in the price range. Printing quality, more beautiful and varied colors, and sharpness of the image may make a particular card much more desirable and, therefore, it will command a higher price.

Cards that have a wide price range usually are those that are presently the "most wanted" and best sellers. Dealers, most often, will only offer a small discount when selling these because they know there is a good market for them. Cards listed with a narrow price range are usually those that have been "hot" but have settled down and established a more competitive trading range. Dealer discounting on these slow-movers tends to be much more prevalent than those in the wide price ranges.

GUIDELINES FOR BUYING AND SELLING CARDS

As noted above, the prices listed in this price guide are retail prices—prices that a collector can expect to pay when buying a card from a dealer. It is up to the collectors to bargain for any available discount from the dealer.

The wholesale price is the price which a collector can expect from a dealer when selling cards. This price will be significantly lower than the retail price. Most dealers try to operate on a 100% markup and will normally pay around 50% of a card's low retail value. On some high-demand cards, he might pay up to 60% or 75% if he wants them badly enough.

Dealers are always interested in purchasing collections and accumulations of cards. They are primarily interested in those that were issued before 1915, but may be induced to take those issued afterwards if they are clean and in good condition.

Collections: Normally, collections are a specialized group or groups of cards that a person has built over the years. They will be in nice condition, without any damage, and may contain some rarities or high-demand cards.

Collectors wanting to sell their cards may need to contact a dealer in order to dispose of them. As noted above, be prepared to sell at approximately 50% of the value of the collection. If you do not know of any dealers, write the **International Federation of Postcard Dealers,** to the attention of Mildred Knoll, Secretary, P. O. Box 3587, Baltimore, Maryland 21214, and enclose a double-stamped, self-addressed #10 envelope for a list of members.

Another source for disposing of your collection would be dealers who advertise in *Barr's Post Card News,* 70 South 6th St., Lansing, IA 52151 or *Postcard Collector,* P.O. Box 1050, Dubuque, IA 52004. Other publications that have postcard sections are *Collectors News,* P. O. Box 156, Grundy Center, IA 50638-0156, *Paper Collectors' Market Place,* P. O. Box 128, Scandinavia, WI 54977, and *The Antique Trader,* P. O. Box 1050, Dubuque, IA 52004. Write to any of these publications and ask for information on subscriptions or sample copies.

Accumulations: Accumulations are usually groups of many different kinds, many different eras, and many different topics ... with the good usually mixed in with the bad. If you have a large accumulation that you wish to sell, your best bet is to contact a dealer as noted above. You may expect only 20% to 30% of value on a group such as this. Many low demand cards are non-sellers and are worthless to a dealer, but he may take them if there are some good cards in the accumulation.

Buying: Without doubt, the best way to buy postcards is to attend a show where there is a large group of dealers. Compare prices among dealers on cards that are of interest to you, and return to those who have the best cards at the lowest price for your purchases. Buy from a dealer in your area if there is one. A good dealer will help you with your collection by searching for cards you need or want. If none are available, many dealers listed in *Barr's Post Card News* and *Postcard Collector* run auctions or will send cards on approval. Also, you might try joining a postcard club. It is possible to find an excellent choice of cards at these meetings because attendees bring material that is of interest to their fellow members.

It is also possible to find cards at Antique Shows, Flea Markets and Antique Shops. You can, however, waste a lot of time and never find suitable cards. It is best to go direct to the source and that would be a postcard dealer or auctioneer. Here you can find a great variety and, almost always, cards of interest to you.

IDENTIFYING THE AGE OF POSTCARDS

The dating of postcards for years or eras of issue can be accurately determined if the card is studied for identity points. Research has already been done by earlier historians and guidelines have been put into place.

There were seven eras for the postcard industry and each one has distinguishing points to help establish its respective identity. The following helps determine the era of the card in question.

PIONEER ERA (1893-1898)

The Pioneer Era began when picture postcards were placed on sale by vendors and exhibitors at the Colombian Exposition in Chicago, May, 1893. These were very popular and proved to be a great success. The profitable and lasting future of the postcard was greatly enhanced. The cards from this era are relatively scarce. They can be identified by combinations of the following:
- All have undivided backs.
- None show the "Authorized by Act of Congress" byline.
- Postal cards will have the Grant or Jefferson head stamp.
- Most, but not all, will be multiple view cards.
- The words "Souvenir of ..." or "Greetings from..." appear on many.
- Postage rate, if listed, is usually 2 cents.
- The most common titles will be "Souvenir Card" or "Mail Card."
- Appeared mostly in the big Eastern cities.

PRIVATE MAILING CARD ERA (1898-1901)

On May 19, 1898, the government gave private printers permission to print and sell postcards. These cards were all issued with the inscription "Private Mailing Card," and today they are referred to as PMC's. It is easy to identify these because of the inscription. It may be noted that many of the early Pioneer views were reprinted as Private Mailing Cards.

UNDIVIDED BACK ERA (1901-1907)

On December 24, 1901, permission was given for use of the wording "Post Card" to be imprinted on the backs of privately printed cards. All cards during this era had undivided backs and only the address was to appear on the back. The message, therefore, had to be written on the front (picture side) of the card. For this reason, there is writing on the face of many cards; this is becoming more acceptable on cards of this era.

DIVIDED BACK ERA (1907-1915)

This era came into being on March 1, 1907. The divided back made it possible for both the address and the message to be on the back of the card. This prevented the face of the card from being written on and proved to be a great boon for collectors. Normally the view colors or images filled the entire card with no white border.

WHITE BORDER ERA (1915-1930)

The White Border Era brought an end to the postcard craze era. The golden age ended as imports from Germany ceased and publishers in the U.S. began printing postcards to try to fill the void. The cards were very poor quality and many were reprints of earlier Divided Back Era cards. These are easily distinguished by the white border around the pictured area.

LINEN ERA (1930-1945)

Improvements in American printing technology brought improved card quality. Publishers began using a linen-like paper containing a high rag content but used very cheap inks in most instances. Until recently, these cards were considered very cheap by collectors. Now they are very popular with collectors of Roadside America, Blacks,

Comics, and Advertising. Views are also becoming more popular as collectors realize that this era too is a part of our history, and these cards help to illustrate the changes in the geographic structure of America.

PHOTOCHROME ERA (1939 to present day)

"Modern Chromes," as they are now called by the postcard fraternity, were first introduced in 1939. Publishers, such as **Mike Roberts, Dexter Press, Curt Teich,** and **Plastichrome**, began producing cards that had very beautiful chrome colors and were very appealing to collectors. The growth of this group has been spectacular in recent years, so much so that there are now many postcard dealers who specialize only in chromes.

REAL PHOTO POSTCARDS (1900 to present day)

Real Photo postcards were in use as early as 1900. It is sometimes very hard to date a card unless it has been postally used or dated by the photographer. The stamp box will usually show the process by which it was printed—**AZO, EKC, KODAK, VELOX**, and **KRUXO** are some of the principal ones. Careful study of photo cards is essential to make sure they have not been reproduced.

HOW TO DETERMINE CARD VALUES

Values of each card are listed under the headings "VG" (Very Good) and "EX" (Excellent). If there is no value listed for a card, just refer to the one listed immediately above it.

Example:	A-3146	10 - 15	15 - 18
	A-3147		

The value of A-3147 would also be $10 - 15 and $15 - 18.

Visit Our Web Sites on the Internet for All Colonial House Price Guides and Want Lists for Postcards

---

Colonial House Publishers, P. O. Box 609, Enka, NC 28728
Phone: 704-667-1427 • Fax: 704-667-1111
EMail:JMashb0135@aol.com
Web Sites: http://www.postcard-books.com or
http://www.csmonline.com/colonialhouse

FAIRY REVELS

This image by Fannie May Anderson (Florence Mary
Anderson) exemplifies fairies as they are perceived today.
It was published by Vivian Mansell & Company,
Series 2115, and is called "Fairy Revels."

Chapter 2

Fairies

The fairy family includes brownies, elves, gnomes, goblins, fairies, leprechauns, nixes, pixies, poltergeists, sprites and trolls.

A fairy, by definition, is a small imaginary creature that interferes in human affairs. People have known about them since the Middle Ages and many still believe in them today. They were thought to be helpful but also mischievous. With their magical powers they could appear and disappear at will. They could take the shape of humans or animals, cast spells, and change the shape of people.

Since the 1400's, people in most parts of the world have believed in fairies. Some have believed that fairies lived for hundreds of years, and others said they lived forever. English folklore tells of fairies who lived in very special places such as caves, springs, mountains, woods or buildings. Others lived in a particular organized society in a land of magical charm and fantasy called *Fairyland.* These are the predominant types that the artists of the Golden Years of Postcards chose to paint, and these ideas still dominate works up to this time.

There were basically two different groups of fairies. **Noble Fairies** formed the royal court and held various titles just as people do in a kingdom. The king was Oberon and his queen was Titania, a beautiful lady with wings. They lived in a little palace, commanded a little fairy army, and had fairy lords and ladies, as can be seen in the series *Titania's Palace.* Noble fairies loved to dance and were known to dance all night in the moonlight.

Household Fairies came from the imagination of the common folk, and these fairies usually interfered with activities of people at home or at work. Household fairies include elves, goblins, kobolds (German), leprechauns, nixes (water), pixies, poltergeists and trolls. Most household fairies did good deeds but they also liked to play tricks; many tales are told of their mischief around the house and in the fields.

There are a tremendous number of beautiful fairy cards by many wonderful artists. The works of Ida Outhwaite, Hilda Miller, Millicent Sowerby and Margaret Tarrant are particularly outstanding and very much in demand. Their fairies were specifically painted for the pleasure of children of their era. However, today they are enjoyed by much older "beholders of fairies in a fantasy world."

FAIRIES

	VG	EX
ANDERSON, FANNIE MAY (Florence Mary) (G.B.)		
Vivian Mansell & Co.		
Series 2115 (6)		
"The Artist at Home"	$ 20 - 25	$ 25 - 28
"The Elfin Pipes"		
"Fairy Revels"		

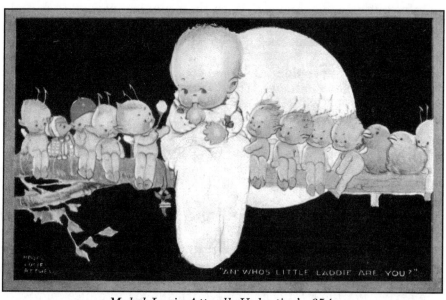

Mabel Lucie Attwell, Valentine's 654
"And Who's Little Laddie Are You?"

M. L. Attwell, Valentine's A396
"Somebody said there are no..."

M. L. Attwell, Valentine's 656
"Please Don't Pick Our Houses."

"The Key to the Moon"
"The Moonchild"
Other

ANICHINI, EZIO (Italy)
  Ballerini & Fratini
    Series 351 Fairies — 18 - 22 — 22 - 25

ATTWELL, MABEL L. (G.B.)
  Valentine & Sons
    Card No.

J8 "Suppose a Fairy Came and He..."	15 - 20	20 - 22
A393 "I'se Just Arrived"	20 - 25	25 - 28
395X "May all your Sweetest Dreams..."	18 - 22	22 - 25
A396 "Somebody said there are no fairies"	20 - 25	25 - 28
652 "See what I'se brought...Fairyland"	20 - 25	25 - 28
616 "Hullo"	12 - 15	15 - 18
651 "Hurry up for the Last Train..."	20 - 22	22 - 25
654 "And Who's Little Laddie are You?"		
A653 "Star Fishing!"		
A655 "S'cuse Me - Do you give flying..."	18 - 22	22 - 25
656 "Please Don't Pick Our Houses"		
667 "And that's the tale you told..."	12 - 15	15 - 18
796 "Another New Day to be Glad in..."		
1167 "May a Fairy Ring of Happiness..."		
1439 "There are Fairies at the Bottom..."		

Die Vöglein im Walde

Fritz Baumgarten, Oppel & Hess 1509-2
"Die Vögleim im Walde"

1547 "Those are Fairies"		
1669 "Good Morning to you!"		
1868 "Have you ever heard the flutter..."		
2028 "I'm hoping good Fairies are well..."	20 - 22	22 - 25
A4785 "What are little girls made of?"	15 - 18	18 - 22
A4934 "Oo-My! Can't oo Fly?"	22 - 25	25 - 28
5226 "I'm tired of being a Fairy"	10 - 12	12 - 15
5320 "Away with Troubles"		
5359 "When God made the World..."	15 - 18	18 - 22
5656 "I'll soon learn 'em I'm around"	10 - 12	12 - 15

BARHAM, SYBIL (G.B.)
  C. W. Faulkner

Series 1859 "Fairies" (6)	10 - 12	12 - 14

BAUMGARTEN, FRITZ (Germany)
  Oppel & Hess, Jena

Series 1509 (6)	12 - 15	15 - 18
Series 1502, 1514, 1534 (6)		
Series 5179, 5192, 5195 (6)		
Other Publishers	10 - 12	12 - 15

BERGER, Series 116 (B&W)   15 - 20   20 - 25

BOWDEN, DORIS (G.B.)
  C.W. Faulkner & Co.
    Series 1811 (6)

"A Plump Little Girl"	18 - 22	22 - 25
Others		

BRETT, MOLLY (G.B.)

C. W. Faulkner & Co. Series 1984	35 - 40	40 - 50
Medici Society "Playtime" Series	10 - 12	12 - 15

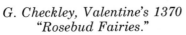

G. Checkley, Valentine's 1370
"Rosebud Fairies."

Rene Cloke, Valentine's 1848
"The Daisy Fairy."

CHECKLEY, GLADYS (G.B.)
> **Valentine & Sons**
>> **Series 1370 "Fairy School"** (6)
>>> "Autumn Frolics"   12 - 15   15 - 18
>>> "Fairies in the Orchard"
>>> "The Fairies' Shelter"
>>> "Rosebud Fairies"

CLOKE, RENE (G.B)
> **Valentine & Sons**
>> **Series 1002 "Fairies"** (6)   15 - 20   20 - 25
>> **Series 1183**
>> **Series 1848**
>> **Series 5372-77** (6)
> **J. Salmon, Ltd.**
>> **Series 4626** (6)   6 - 8   8 - 10
>> **Series 4627** (6)   8 - 10   10 - 12

COWHAM, HILDA (G.B.)
> **C.W. Faulkner & Co.**
>> **Series 1918 "Fairies"** (6)
>>> "The Fairy Castle"   18 - 22   22 - 25
>>> "Follow My Leader"
>>> "The Mean..."
>>> "Where Fairies Come From"
>>> Others

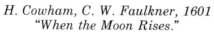

When the Moon rises.

H. Cowham, C. W. Faulkner, 1601
"When the Moon Rises."

Josephine Duddle, G.A. & Co.,
Series 136-2, No Caption

Series 1601 "The Fairy Glen" (6)		
"The Fairy Glen"	18 - 22	22 - 25
"The Fairy Revel"		
"Into the hollow of the hill"		
"When the Moon Rises"		
DAUSTY		
C. & P. & Co.		
Series 704 "Nymphs" (6)	8 - 10	10 - 12
DIELITZ "Alpen Fairy"	12 - 15	15 - 18
DUDDLE, JOSEPHINE (G.B.)		
G.A. & Co., Ltd.		
Series 136-2	15 - 20	20 - 25
FORCK, ELSBETH (Germany)		
Hermann A. Peters		
"Gnomen-u. Elfinreich" Silhouettes	12 - 15	15 - 18
GIRIS, CESAR (Italy)		
Raphael Tuck		
Series 2365 "Madame Butterfly" (6)	18 - 20	20 - 25
GOVEY, A. (G.B.)		
Humphrey Milford		
"Dreams & Fairies" Series (6)		
"Hugh and Hilda by the Stream"	25 - 28	28 - 32
"This is a game called..."		
"This is Young Basil the Brave"		

A Pixie made a chain of flowers,
And hung it in a tree,
And swinging there the whole day long,
He sang a little Fairy Song,
A.M.S.   As happy as could be.

When Fairies dance at twilight time,
The Golden Moon is low,
And fluttering round in magic rings,
The moonlight gleaming on their wings,
A.M.S.   The Dainty Fairies go.

L. M. Hine, A. & C. Black, Ltd.
"A Pixie Made a Chain of ..."

L. M. Hine, A. & C. Black, Ltd.
"When Fairies Dance at ..."

"When Pussy and Jackie..."
Other
F.H. (G.B.)
   Vivian Mansell & Co.
      Series 2114 (6)
      "Almost Fairy Time"   15 - 18   18 - 22
      "Mischief"
      "The Lost Fairy"
      "The Moon Maiden"
      "The Fisherman"
      Other
HAIG, BERYL (G.B.)   12 - 15   15 - 18
HINE, L. M. (G.B.)
   A. & C. Black, London
      "A Pixie made a chain of flowers..."   32 - 35   35 - 40
      "A Pretty Fairy Mother..."
      "Some Fairies found some Bubbles..."
      "Some Fairies met a Butterfly..."
      "When Fairies Dance at Twilight..."
      "When Fairies find a Tiny Pool..."
KENNEDY, TOM or TK (G.B.)
   W. & K., London (Wildt & Kray)
      Series 5234 "Fairies" (6)
      "Blue Bell"   15 - 18   18 - 22

Paul Konewka, Ackermann's 110
1406, "Titania und Zettel"

Paul Konewka, Ackermann's 110
1403, "Titania"

TK (Tom Kennedy), W&K 5234
"Butterfly."

Alice Marshall, R. Tuck Ser. 3490
"Oh! To be lost in Fairyland"

"Butterfly"
"The Honey Bee"
"Little Pansy Blossom"
"Violets"

KOIVU, RUDOLF (Germany)
   "The Goldfish" Fairy   20 - 25   25 - 30

KONEWKA, PAUL (Germany)
  F.A. Ackerman
    Series 110 (12 Silhouettes)
    1403 "Titania"   22 - 25   25 - 28
    1406 "Titania und Zettel"

MAILICK, A. (Germany)
    Fairy sits on big mushroom   25 - 30   30 - 35

MARGETSON, HESTER (G.B.)
  Vivian Mansell & Co.
    Series 2127 (6)
    "A Voyage of Discovery"   15 - 18   18 - 22
    "The Little Ferry Man"
    Series 2129 (6)
    "The Fairy Ballet"   15 - 18   18 - 22
    "The Moon Fairy"
    "A Really Truly Fairy"
    Others
  Humphrey Milford
    Fairy Series (6)   20 - 25   25 - 28

MARSH-LAMBERT, H.G.C. (G.B.)
  A.M. Davis & Co.
    Series 519 "Flower Fairies" (6)   15 - 18   18 - 22
  C.W. Faulkner
    Series 1400 (6)   10 - 12   12 - 15
    Series 1510 (6)   12 - 15   15 - 18

MARSHALL, ALICE (G.B.)
  Raphael Tuck
    Series 3489 "Fairyland Fancies I" (6)
    "Hie away 'neath shades of night..."   30 - 35   35 - 38
    "Maids and lovers we befriend..."
    "Oh to be with you in the wondrous..."
    "Tis now the Witching Hour of Night"
    "Weaving a Web of Golden Fancies"
    "What's O'Clock? And I'll be there!"
    Series 3490 "Fairyland Fancies" II (6)
    "Let me build a Castle"   30 - 35   35 - 38
    "Oh! To be lost in Fairyland"
    "Lost in Wonderland"
    "On Fairy Wings to Happy Land"
    Series 3489 (6)   18 - 20   20 - 26

MAUSER, PHYLLIS (G.B.)
  P. Salmon
    Series 5159, "Brownies & Fairies" (6)   8 - 10   10 - 12

This is a beautiful anonymous series of gold embossed flower fairies in the art nouveau vein. No publisher or artist is listed; the series number is 247.

The captions tell of a courtship which leads to marriage.

"One -
I Love"

"Two -
He Loves"

"Three -
We Love, I Say"

"Four -
He Comes"

"Five -
He Tarries"

"Six -
He Loves and Marries"

Thomas Maybank, R. Tuck, "Midsummer Dreams"
Series 6683, "A Thought"

MAYBANK, THOMAS (G.B.)
   Raphael Tuck
      Series 6683 "Midsummer Dreams" (6)

"A Few Lines"	25 - 28	28 - 32
"A Thought"		
"Just a Note"		

MILLER, HILDA (G.B.)
   C.W. Faulkner & Co.
      Series 1690 "Fairies" (6)

"Catch Me!"	22 - 25	25 - 28
"The Enchanted Bubbles"		
"The Entrance to Fairy Land"		
"Up and Down! Up and Down!"		
"Upon a Snail Coach I ride in State"		
"Within the Enchanted Glade"		

      Series 1693 "Fairies" (6)

"The Fairy Flight"	22 - 25	25 - 28
"A Fairy Vision"		
"Filling the air with Fairy Forms"		
"The Fairy in the Blossom"		
"Joining in the Fairy Revel"		
"Within the Magic Circle"		

      Series 1822 "Peter Pan" (6)   15 - 18   18 - 20

MÜLLER, PAUL L. (Germany)
   Oscar Heierman, Berlin (Novitas)
      Series 550 "Gnomes" (6)

"The lesson of song"	10 - 12	12 - 15

*Hilda T. Miller, C. W. Faulkner
1693, "Joining in the Fairy Revel"*

*A. Penot, I. Lapina, Paris 1340
"Red Butterfly" (Fairy)*

*Hilda T. Miller, C. W. Faulkner Series 1690
"Upon a Snail Coach I Ride in State."*

I. R. Outhwaite, A. & C. Black 72
"Tossing up the Rainbow Bubbles"

I. R. Outhwaite, A. & C. Black
71A, "The Witch"

OUTHWAITE, IDA R. (Australia)
    A. & C. Black Ltd., London

Series 71 "The Enchanted Forest" (6)		
by I. R. & G. Outhwaite		
"The Butterfly Chariot"	22 - 25	25 - 28
"Good-bye to Patty"		
Others		
Series 71-A "Elves & Fairies" (6)		
"Fairy Frolic"	25 - 28	28 - 32
"The Glowlamp Fairy"		
"The Nautilus Fairy"		
"Serena's Wedding"		
"They stood still in front of her"		
"The Witch"		
Series 72 "Fairyland" (6)		
"Butterfly Ferry"	25 - 28	28 - 32
"Catching the Moon"		
"Listening to the Nightingale"		
"Tossing up the Rainbow Bubbles"		
Others		
Series 73 "Bunny and Brownie" (6)		
"Driving the others with reins..."	28 - 32	32 - 35
"Fairies were dancing in and out."		

The Nautilus Fairy.

I. R. Outhwaite, A. & C. Black 71A
"The Nautilus Fairy"

"Playing with the bubbles"		30 - 35	35 - 40
"Round the grass-tuft...a Pearly Shell"		28 - 32	32 - 35
"She was rather severe with George"			
Other			
Series 74 "Blossom" (6)			
"A little mist played over the Pond"		28 - 32	32 - 35
"The frogs learn to jump..."			
"One on a huge Dragon-Fly"			
"She is a Spring Fairy"			
* "Seated on the edge of a Mauve Crocus"			
"What is time Bus?"			
* Ad for Black's Postcards on back		35 - 40	40 - 45
Series 75 "The Little Fairy Sister" (6)			
by I. R. and G. Outhwaite			
"Bridget the Fairy Beauty"		28 - 32	32 - 35
"Fairy Beauty rocks a Babe"			
"The Fairy Beauty"			
* "The Fairy Bridget and Kookaburra"			
"The Fairy Bridget and the Merman"			
"Periwinkle painting the Petals"			
* Ad for Black's Postcards on back		35 - 40	40 - 45
Series 76 "The Enchanted Forest" (6)			
by I. R. and G. Outhwaite			
"Anne plays the pipes"		25 - 30	30 - 35
"Drawn along by Fishes"			
"Patty talks to forest creatures"			
"The Witch's Sister on her broom"			
"The Witch on her broom"			

I. R. Outhwaite, A. & C. Black 72
"Listening to the Nightingale"

I. R. Outhwaite, A. & C. Black 73
"Playing with Bubbles"

I. R. Outhwaite, A. & C. Black 73
"Round the Grass Tuft Glided..."

I. R. Outhwaite, A. & C. Black 74
"A little mist played over..."

Series 79 "The Little Road to Fairyland" (6)
by A.R. Rentoul and I. R. Outhwaite

"Anne rides on a Nautilus Shell"	28 - 32	32 - 35
"The farthest one looked like..."		
"The little one took it's paws..."		
"She flew through the window..."		
"What a fright she got"		

PENOT, A. (France)
I. Lapina, Paris

1340 "Red Butterfly" (Fairy)	20 - 25	25 - 30

PEYK, H. (Germany) (1950's)

R.H.F. 758 No Captions	8 - 10	10 - 12

PLUMSTEAD, JOYCE (G.B.)
Vivian Mansell & Co.
Series 2126 (6)

"Autumn Leaves"	10 - 12	12 - 15
"Fairy Clocks"		
"Fairy Umbrellas"		
"The Fairy Shoemaker"		
"The Pixie's Airmail"		

PURSER, PHYLLIS M. (G.B.)
J. Salmon, Ltd. (1950's)

5155 "A tap upon the window pane..."	8 - 10	10 - 12

I. R. Outhwaite, A. & C. Black 76
"Anne Plays the Pipes"

I. R. Outhwaite, A. & C. Black 76
"The Witch's Sister on Her..."

H. Peyk, RHF 758
No Caption

Phyllis Purser, J. Salmon, Ltd.
5158, "A Sleepy Boy said..."

5156 "One night when we..."
5157 "We didn't invite Him..."
5158 "A Sleepy Boy said Pixie One..."
5189 "Buttercups and Daisies..."

RICHARD, J. (G.B.)
  C.W. Faulkner & Co.
    Series 2010 (6)
    "The Warrior Bold"   22 - 25   25 - 28
    Others

RICHARDSON, AGNES (G.B.)
  C. W. Faulkner & Co.
    Series 1233 "The Swing Fairies" (6)   18 - 22   22 - 25
  Inter-Art Co.
    "Comique" Series 4960 (Uns.) (6)   15 - 18   18 - 22
  Raphael Tuck
    Series 1649 (6)
    "They are Sweethearts..."   22 - 25   25 - 28
    "There really are Fairies you know..."
    Series 1850 (6)
    "Round and Round, Round and Round..."   18 - 22   22 - 25
    Series 3244 "Once Upon a Time" (6)
    "The Fairies say you love me, Dear..."   22 - 25   25 - 28
    Series 1650 (6)
    "I'm telling a tale to the Bunnies..."   18 - 22   22 - 25

Agnes Richardson, R. Tuck 3244
"The fairies say you love me..."

J. Richard, C. W. Faulkner 2010
"The Warrior Bold"

Series 3447 (6)	16 - 18	18 - 20
ROSE, FREDA M. (G.B.)		
J. Salmon, Ltd.		
Fairy Series (6)		
4544 "Dance of the Daisy Chain"	12 - 15	15 - 18
4547 "Sunrise"		
4548 "Woodland Sprites"		
4549 "Waking up the Crocus"		
Others		
SCHERMELE, WILLY (Netherlands)		
Series 390	10 - 12	12 - 15
SCHMUCKER, SAMUEL L. (U.S.)		
Detroit Publishing Co., 1907 (Uns.)		
"Fairy Queen" Series or "Mottos" (6)		
14659 "Roses" - by Rosseth	250 - 300	300 - 350
14660 "Harmony" - by Thomas Moore		
14661 "Captive" - by Coleridge		
14662 "Youth's Garden" - by Herrick		
14663 "Unafraid" - by Shakespeare		
14664 "Philomeis" - by Byron		
"Gnome" Series (6) (Uns.)		
1 Hummingbird	150 - 175	175 - 200
2 Bee		
3 Mouse		

THE "FAIRY QUEEN" OR "MOTTOS" SERIES
BY
S. L. SCHMUCKER (UNSIGNED)

PUBLISHED BY DETROIT PUBLISHING COMPANY

14659
"Roses"
Rossetti

14660
"Harmony"
Thomas Moore

14661
"Captive"
Coleridge

14662
"Youth's Garden"
Herrick

14663
"Unafraid"
Shakespeare

14664
"Philomeis"
Byron

Eric Schutz, B.K.W.I. 165-4
No Caption

Eric Schutz, B.K.W.I. 165-5
No Caption

Eric Schutz, B.K.W.I. 165-1
No Caption

Eric Schutz, B.K.W.I. 165-6
"Blümchen Wunderhold"

4 Frog
5 Beetle
6 Owl
SCHUTZ, ERIC (Austria)
  B.K.W.I.

Series 165 "Fairy Nudes" (6)		
1 Nude lies on sunflower	28 - 32	32 - 35
2 "Sommergalute"		
3 Nude lies on poppy blossom		
4 Blonde nude in zinnia blossom		
5 Nude sits on Lily blossom		
6 "Blumenkonigin" Nude sits on rose		
Series 391 (6)	18 - 20	20 - 25

  M. Munk, Vienna

Series 1363 (6)	15 - 18	18 - 22
Series 1364 (6)		
Series 1365 (6)		
Series 435 (6) Uns. Andersen's Fairy Tales	18 - 20	20 - 25

SHERBORNE, M. (G.B.)
  Salmon & Co. 1940's Era

Series 4239 "Fairies of the Wood"	10 - 12	12 - 15
Series 5186 "Fairy Feast"	8 - 10	10 - 12
1960's Era "Fairies of the Garden"	6 - 8	8 - 10

SOWERBY, MILLICENT (G.B.)
  Humphrey Milford, London

"Bird Children" (6)		
"Good Gracious Me!..."	25 - 28	28 - 32
"Hark, Mister Owl!..."		
"Kingfisher Green..."		
"When Robin Sings Above..."		
"When the First Star..."		
"When the First Swallows..."		
"Fairy Frolic" Series (6)		
"This Fay among the berries swings..."	25 - 28	28 - 32
"The Summer Elves"		
"This Springtime Fairy Pipes..."		
"When Crocuses and Snowdrops Peep..."		
"When Winter Comes..."		
"Flower Children" (6)		
"Day-Lily"	25 - 28	28 - 32
"Evening Primrose"		
"King-Cups"		
"Love-in-a-Mist"		
"Pansies"		
"Snowdrop"		
"Flower Fairies" (6)		
"Says Jolly Red-cap in the Tree..."	25 - 28	28 - 32
"This Elf and Field-Mouse Play..."		

THIS SPRINGTIME FAIRY PIPES SO GAY
UPON THE APPLE BLOSSOM BOUGH,
THE LAMBS, BENEATH HIM, FRISK & PLAY-
THE OTHER FAIRY SHOWS THEM HOW.
J.P.

M. Sowerby, H. Milford, Fairy Frolic, "This Springtime Fairy..."

HEDGEROW ELVES IN ROSES SLEEP
TILL THE EARLY SUNBEAMS PEEP.~
TILL THE SWALLOWS COME AND CRY-
'PLAY WITH US AT 'TIP AND FLY.'~
J.P.

M. Sowerby, H. Milford, Merry Elves, "Hedgerow Elves in Roses..."

TWO DICKY BIRDS SAT ON A BLACKBERRY BOUGH,
AND THEY TWITTERED A SONG TOGETHER-
'INDEED, MASTER ELF, YOU LOOK ELEGANT NOW
WITH THAT BEAUTIFUL PEACOCKS FEATHER!'
J.P.

M. Sowerby, H. Milford, Merry Elves, "Two Dicky Birds Sat..."

TO SWING OVER POPPIES IS NICE -
ON THE TAILS OF TWO JOLLY DORMICE.
THE DORMICE DONT MIND IT AT ALL,
AND THEY WONT LET THE FAIRYKIN FALL.

M. Sowerby, H. Milford, Woodland Games, "To Swing ..."

YELLOW ARE MY WINGS AS BUTTER.
OVER EVERY FLOWER I FLUTTER:~
FOR I FEEL IT IS MY DUTY ~ ~ ~
TO BEWITCH THEM WITH MY BEAUTY.

I'M JUST AS BLUE AS BLUE CAN BE.~~
THE COLOUR OF THE SKY AND SEA. ~
I LOVE TO PERCH ON STATELY THISTLES.
SAYS CATERPILLAR : "MIND THE BRISTLES!"

M. Sowerby, Milford, Pretty Wings,
" 'Brimstone' and Caterpillar"

M. Sowerby, H. Milford, Pretty
Wings, " 'Clifton Blue' and ..."

KINGFISHER GREEN AND KINGFISHER BLUE.
PLEASE, MAY WE GO A-FISHING WITH YOU?
WE'LL SIT SO QUIET, NOT MOVE NOR SPEAK.
WE WITH OUR LINES, AND YOU WITH YOUR BEAK!

THE SUMMER ELVES ARE RATHER FOND
OF DIVING IN THE LILY POND ~ ~
THEY DON'T TAKE OFF THEIR CLOTHES, & YET.
THE WATER NEVER MAKES THEM WET.
J.P.

M. Sowerby, H. Milford, Bird
Children, "Kingfisher Green ..."

M. Sowerby, H. Milford, Fairy
Frolic, "The Summer Elves ..."

"Flowers and Wings" (6)
"By Moonlight the Wood Fairies..."   25 - 28   28 - 32
"Daddy Longlegs, Flying Strong..."
"Grasshopper, Grasshopper..."
"Oh Bumble Bee..."
"Says Periwinkle Elf..."
"This Poor Little Elf..."
"Merry Elves" (6)
"At Dawn the Sun..."   25 - 28   28 - 32
"Hedgerow Elves in Roses..."
"This Baby Elf flew..."
"This Elf has found some Grapes..."
"Two Dicky Birds sat..."
"When the Mother Bird..."
"Peter Pan Postcards" (6)
"In the Lost Boys' Cozy Cave..."   22 - 25   25 - 28
"The Lost Boys..."
"Peter Pan is afloat on a nest..."
"To the Velvety Tree Tops..."
"Wendy and Joan and Michael..."
"When Peter Lost his Shadow..."
"Pretty Wings" (6)
"Brimstone" and Caterpillar   28 - 32   32 - 35
"Clifton Blue" and Caterpillar
"Large White" and Caterpillar
"Orange Tip" and Caterpillar
"Peacock" and Caterpillar
"Red Admiral" and Caterpillar
"Sky Fairies" (6)
"This Fairy got up in good time..."   25 - 28   28 - 32
"To See-Saw on a Sunbeam is..."
"Two Sky Fairies are hiding..."
"When Mr. Dustman scatters..."
Others
"Woodland Games" (6)
"Listen Bun. We'll have some fun..."   20 - 25   25 - 28
"Oh come and float on My..."
"The Rules of Fairy Leapfrog..."
"The Elf makes the Squirrels..."
"To swing over Poppies is Nice"
"Two Elves on the Wing..."
"Fairies Friends" Series (6)   22 - 25   25 - 28
SPURGIN, FRED (Latvia - G.B.)
   Inter-Art. Co.
      Series 615 "Fairy" (6)
      "I believe no more in fairies"   15 - 18   18 - 22
   Raphael Tuck Oilette "In Fairyland"
      Series 3032 (6)

"You gave me a smile..."

STEELE, L. R. (G.B.)	15 - 18	18 - 22
Salmon & Co.		
Series 5050-5055 "Famous Fairies" (6)		
5050 "Willo the Wisp"	10 - 12	12 - 15
5053 "Pan"		
5054 "Puck"		
5055 "Neptune"		
"Peeps at Pixie's" Series (6)		
4964 "Pixie Post"	10 - 12	12 - 15
4965 "The Hat Shop"		
4967 "Pixie Market"		
4968 "A Windy Day"		
4969 "Hush a Bye"		
Series 5172-77 (6)	10 - 12	12 - 15
Valentine's		
"Fairy Series" (6)		
1847 "The Vetch Fairy"	10 - 12	12 - 15
1848 "The Daisy Fairy"		
1851 "The Speedwell Fairy"		
1852 "The Bindweed Fairy"		
Others		
SYMONDS, CONSTANCE (G.B.)		
C. W. Faulkner & Co.		
Series 1645 (6)		
"Do you love Butter?"	15 - 18	18 - 20
"The Duet"		
"Fairy Piper"		
"The Morning Walk"		
"The Punt"		
"Wake Up"		
Series 1926 (6)		
"A Difficult Cuckoo"	20 - 22	22 - 25
Series 1957 (6)		
Blue Periwinkle "Early Friendship"		
Series 1958 (6)		
American Starwort - "Welcome Stranger"	18 - 22	22 - 25
Blue Convolvuloua - "Night"		
Bundles of Reeds - "Music"		
Guelder Rose - "Snow"		
Heather - "Solitude"		
Michaelmas Daisies - "Farewell"		
TARRANT, MARGARET (G.B.)		
Medici Society*		
PK 120 "The Fairy Troupe"	8 - 10	10 - 12
PK 184 "The Enchantress"		
* Medici Cards Reissued	3 - 4	4 - 5
UNTERSBERGER, ANDREAS (Germany)		
Emil Kohn, München		

L. R. Steele, J. Salmon, Ltd. 5055
Famous Fairies, "Neptune..."

Constance Symonds, C. W.
Faulkner 1645, "Fairy Piper."

Fairy and Gnome Series (12)		
1126 "Der Tanz mit dem Irrwischweibchen"	12 - 15	15 - 18
1129 "Der Rauchkunftler"	12 - 15	15 - 18
Others		
T.S.N. (Theo. Stroefer, Nürnberg)		
Series 2005-2 (3)		
"Verboten Fruchte"	12 - 15	15 - 18
Others		
WATKINS, DOROTHY (G.B.)		
Valentine & Sons		
Series 6 "The Dance of the Elves"	8 - 10	10 - 12
WEIGAND, MARTIN (Austria)		
Percy Hein		
Series 1200, Gnomes, Mushrooms (12)	15 - 20	20 - 25
1215 "Der Störenfried"		
1218 "Blumenorakel"		
Others		
Raphael Tuck		
Oilette Series 5583 (6)	15 - 18	18 - 22
"Mid-Summer Dreams" Series (6)	15 - 20	20 - 25
Valentine & Sons		
Series 108 (6	15 - 20	20 - 25
WHEELER, DOROTHY (G.B.)		
Bamforth & Co.		

Martin Weigand, Percy Hein 1215
"Der Störenfried"

Martin Weigand, Percy Hein 1218
"Blumenorakel"

Series 1 "Fairy Secrets" (6)	12 - 15	15 - 18
WHITE, FLORA (G.B.)		
P. Salmon		
Series 4419 (6)	18 - 22	22 - 25
WIELANDT, MANUEL (Germany)		
"Gandalin"	12 - 15	15 - 18
"Das Sommermärchen"		
"Das Wintermärchen"		
"Die Wasserkufe"		
"Pervonte"		
WILLIAMS, MADGE (G.B.)		
J. Salmon, Ltd.		
Series 5305 - 5310 (6)	12 - 15	15 - 18
Series 4740 - 4745 (6)	15 - 18	18 - 22
Valentine & Sons		
"Fairy" Series (6)		
6044 "We all Love it Here"	12 - 15	15 - 18
6045 "This One's for you Dear"		
6046 "Off to see the Sights"		
6047 "Here We are - enjoying..."		
6048 "Wish You were coming too"		
6049 "We're off for Our Holidays"		
Raphael Tuck Series 1160		
"Easter Brownies"	8 - 10	10 - 12

Anonymous Chromolithograph
The Snail Fairy, No Caption

Anonymous Art Nouveau
Chromolithograph, No Caption

PUBLISHERS

M. Munk, Vienna
    Series 1363 Butterfly Fairies (6)   15 - 18   18 - 22
    Series 1364 Butterfly Fairies (6)
    Series 1365 Butterfly Fairies (6)
A. Sockl, Vienna
    Series 6, No. 28
    Fairy types sit on Tiffany vase stands   15 - 20   20 - 25
Theo. Stroefer, Nürnberg
    Series XII, No. 5719
    Fairy types sit on Tiffany vase stands   15 - 20   20 - 25
ANONYMOUS
    Elves   5 - 8   8 - 15
    Fairies   8 - 10   10 - 15
    Gnomes   6 - 8   8 - 12
    Goblins (Usually Halloween)   10 - 12   12 - 15
    Leprechauns   5 - 7   7 - 12
    Nixes
    Pixies   8 - 10   10 - 15
    Poltergeists
    Sprites   7 - 8   8 - 10
    Trolls
Chromolithographs, add $10

E. Kutzer, Bund der Deutschen 373 (Poster Card)
"Rotkäppchen" (Red Riding Hood)

Chapter 3

Fairy Tales & Nursery Rhymes

A fairy tale usually begins with "Once upon a time ..." or "Long, long ago and far away..." and certain features appear over and over with great similarity. There are usually both good and bad characters ...the good character gets in trouble by breaking some kind of "don't do so and so" law and eventually meets up with the bad character. However, the bad character is soon either transformed or killed. In the end good prevails and hero or heroine "live happily ever after."

Each country has its own fairy tales, but each tale resembles those of other countries. The differences are the storytellers that change the names and add some details or spice to make it more exciting or more appealing to the inhabitants of their particular country.

Perhaps the earliest collection of fairy tales was Charles Perrault's *Tales of Mother Goose* published in France in 1697. The Grimm Brothers collected theirs in Germany and their book, *Grimm's Fairy Tales* was published around 1815. Hans Christian Andersen of Denmark completed his collection in 1872. Beautiful postcards of these various fairy tales began appearing between 1895 and 1900 in Germany and Austria, and the rest is history. The early German Chromolithographs and Poster cards, issued before 1910, are classics and are in great demand by today's collector.

The stories of *Tom Thumb, Hansel & Gretel, Sleeping Beauty, Little Red Riding Hood,* etc., can be found on postcards in most all the countries of Europe and Scandinavia; only the language or names are different.

Nursery Rhymes were written for children of all ages. For mothers singing their babies to sleep..."Bye, baby bunting;" to children skipping rope by rhyme...or tongue twisters such as *Peter Piper* for school children. Many beautiful series were issued on postcards. English artists such as Phyllis Cooper, Helen Jackson, M. Sowerby, Willibeek LeMair and H.G.C. Marsh-Lambert head a contingent of wonderful illustrators in a great Fantasy Field!

FAIRY TALES & NURSERY RHYMES

	VG	EX
ATTWELL, MABEL LUCIE (G.B.) (Uns.)		
R. Tuck Series 3328 (6)	$ 20 - 25	$ 25 - 30
R. Tuck Series 3376 (6)		
BANKS, M. E. (G.B.)		
R. Tuck Series 3382 "Paper Dolls" (6)	125 - 150	150 - 175
BARHAM, SYBIL (G.B.)		
Series 1734		
"The Pied Piper of Hamelin" (6)	10 - 12	12 - 15
BARNES, G. L. (G.B)		
Raphael Tuck		
Series 5600 (6) "Cat Studies"		
"Little Bo Peep"	15 - 18	18 - 22
"Little Boy Blue"		
"Little Red Riding Hood"		
"Old King Cole"		
"The Queen of Hearts"		
"Tom, Tom, the Piper's Son"		
Series 5625 "Pussy in Fairyland" (6)		
"A Ten O'Clock Scholar"	18 - 22	22 - 25
"Little Tommy Tucker"		
"Mary, Mary, quite contrary"		
"Old Mother Hubbard"		
"Pat-a-Cake..."		
"Where are you going my Pretty Maid?"		
Series 9301 (6)		
Cats -- Fairy Tales/Nursery Rhymes		
"Little Bo Peep"	15 - 18	18 - 22
"Little Boy Blue"		
"Old King Cole"		
"The Queen of Hearts"		
"Red Riding Hood"		
"The Queen of Hearts"		
"Tom, Tom, the Piper's Son ..."		
BAUMGARTEN, FRITZ (FB) (Germany)		
Opel & Hess		

Ivan Bilibin, "Russian Fairy Tales"
Illustration of a Traditional Russian Folk Hero Poem (1902).

Series 1487 "Hans Im Glück"	10 - 12	12 - 15
Series 1516 "Die Sieben Schwaben"	10 - 12	12 - 15
"Frau Holle"		

BILIBIN, IVAN (Russia)
Russian Fairy Tales, Art Nouveau Style 75 - 100 100 - 125

BORISS, MARGRET (Netherlands)
AMAG
    "Hansel and Gretel" (6) 10 - 12 12 - 15
    "Pied Piper of Hamelin" (6)
    "Puss in Boots" (6)
    "Tom Thumb" (6)

BOWLEY, A. L. (G.B.)
R. Tuck
    Series 3386 "Paper Doll Punchouts" 150 - 175 175 - 200

BRETT, MOLLY (G.B.)
The Medici Society, Ltd., London
    Series 1 (Uns.), **145, 147, 155, 168, 179, 185** 6 - 8 8 - 10

BRUNDAGE, FRANCES (U.S.)
Raphael Tuck
    Series 4095 Little Sunbeams (3) *
    "Little Bo Peep" 35 - 40 40 - 50
    "Little Miss Muffet"
    "Polly and her Kettle"

  * There are 5 other cards in this series which
    are entitled: "Rosy Apples," "Mayblossoms,"
    "The Snow Maiden," "Summer at Sea" and
    "The Little Milk Maid."

Sydney Carter, H. Andersen's
"Eliza and the Swans"

Sydney Carter, H. Andersen's
"The Little Mermaid and Her..."

Phyllis Cooper, R. Tuck 3464
"Where are you going my ..."

Phyllis Cooper, R. Tuck 3463
"Pretty Daisy had a wish ..."

Phyllis Cooper, R. Tuck 3464
"Round and round and round ..."

BURD, C. M.
    Series 18

Fralinger Taffey Nursery Rhymes (24)	30 - 40	40 - 50

CALDECOTT, RANDOLPH (G.B.)
    F. Warne & Co.

48-card set	8 - 10	10 - 12
1970's Reprint of the 48-card set	3 - 4	4 - 5

CARTER, SYDNEY (G.B.)
    "Hans Andersen's Fairy Tales" (6)

"The Bear that played at Soldiers"	15 - 20	20 - 25

    "Eliza and the Swans"
    "Gerda and the Reindeer"
    "The Little Match Seller"
    "The Little Mermaid and Her Five Sisters"
    "Rudy and the Ice Maiden"

COOPER, PHYLLIS (G.B.)
    Raphael Tuck
    "Happy Land" VI, Wooden Children
    Series 3487 (6)

"Dolly Wood and Dolly Dutch..."	20 - 25	25 - 28

    "Susan's Best Friend, Polly May..."
    "To Day Bunny and Molly..."
    "Happy Land" V
    Series 3482 (6)

"Alwite Dearwee I'll be there..."	25 - 28	28 - 32

    "That you are sweet..."
    "In the Spring a Young Man's Fancy..."
    "Some Fellows have all the Luck..."
    "Ah! Said Tommy as he..."
    Series 3486 (6 each)

Series I, Fairy Tales (Rhymes only)	25 - 28	28 - 32

      Series II
      Series III
      Series IV
      Series V
      Series VI
    Nursery Rhymes III
    Series 3488 (6)

"Where are you going my Pretty Maid?"	20 - 25	25 - 28

D.H.C.

Series 790 "Dornröschen" (6)	10 - 12	12 - 15

DOCKAL, H. (Germany)
    UVACHROM

Series 407 (6)	8 - 10	10 - 12

DRAYTON, GRACE (U.S.)
    Reinthal &Newman Nursery Rhymes (6)

488 "O come and be my Lambey dear..."	40 - 45	45 - 50

    489 "O dear me, what do I see..."
    490 "It's nice to be a little boy..."

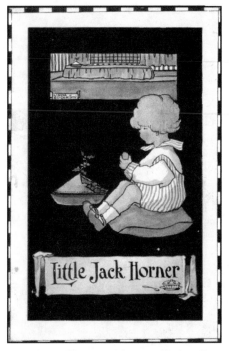

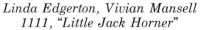

Linda Edgerton, Vivian Mansell
1111, "Little Jack Horner"

Anonymous (Eagle on Back)
"Little Bo-peep has lost her ..."

491 "Little maid neat and sweet..."
492 "Gee up Dobbin -- tried and true..."
493 "The sun is shining warm and sweet..."

EDGERTON, LINDA
  Mansell & Company
    Series 1111   10 - 12   12 - 15
FOLKARD, CHARLES (G.B.)
  A. & C. Black (1940's era)
    Series 80 "Alice in Wonderland" (6)   15 - 18   18 - 22
FORCK, ELSBETH (Germany)
  Oppel & Hess
    Series 1230 Silhouettes
    1 "Dornröschen"   12 - 15   15 - 18
FRISCH-LIEMERK (Austria)
  Deutsch Schulverein, Wien, **Posters**
    60 "Dornröschen"   18 - 22   22 - 25
GOVEY, L.A. (G.B.)
  Humphrey Milford, London
    "Nursery Rhymes from Animal Land" (6)   10 - 12   12 - 15

KATE GREENAWAY

Postcards relating to the works of Kate Greenaway were published
after her death in 1901, and were adapted from her images and

Elsbeth Forck, Oppel & Hess 1230
"Dornröchen"

KG (Kate Greenaway), Anon.
"Humpty Dumpty sat on a ..."

rhymes in Rutledge & Sons' *Mother Goose* and *Old Nursery Rhymes* books which appeared before 1900. Two series have surfaced. One is black and white and the other colored and both are signed KG. Each has a small verse along with the image. These are extremely rare, and few have been seen for sale or in auctions for many years.

The cards have undivided backs, are not numbered, and can only be identified by the verse and Kate's easily recognized images and initialed signature. There are no publisher bylines.

GREENAWAY, KATE (G.B.)
    Colored Series (Signed KG)
        German Undivided Back   150 - 200   200 - 300
    Black & White Series (Signed KG)
        "A dillar, a dollar..."   90 - 100   100 - 125
        "As Tommy Snooks, and Bessie Brooks..."
        "Billie Boy Blue..."
        "Cross Patch, lift the latch..."
        "Elsie Marley has grown so fine..."
        "Girls and boys come out to plat..."
        "Goosey, goosey, gander..."
        "Hark! Hark! The dogs bark..."
        "Here am I, little jumping Joan..."
        "Humpty Dumpty sat on a wall..."

Frisch-Liemerk, Deutsches Schulverein 60
"Dornröschen"

"Jack and Jill went up the hill..."
"Johnny shall have a new bonnet..."
"Little Betty Blue lost her..."
"Little Jack Horner sat in a corner..."
"Little lad, little lad..."
"Mary, Mary, quite contrary..."
"Polly put the kettle on..."
"Ride a cock-horse to Banbury-cross..."
"Ring-a-ring-a-roses..."
"Rock-a-bye baby..."
"There was an old woman..."
"Tom, Tom, the piper's son..."

Listing is incomplete. The above were taken
from an article by Don & Judy McNichols in
What Cheer News, Rhode Island Postcard Club.

GRENGG, M. (Germany)
"Aschenputtel"   10 - 12   12 - 15
"Das Madchen um Meerweibschen"
"Es War einmal ein Zimmergesell"
HP
Deutsches Schulverein   12 - 15   15 - 18

OSKAR HERRFURTH

German artist Oskar Herrfurth was one of the most prolific of all
European Fairy Tales (Märchen) and Tall Tales (Sagen) producers.

O. Herrfurth, Uvachrom 285
"Die Bremer Stadtmusikanten"

O. Herrfurth, Uvachrom 285
"Die Bremer Stadtmusikanten"

He adapted most of the works of The Brothers Grimm, and painted wonderful 6 or 12 card sets which were published by Uvachrom of Stuttgart, Germany. Uvachrom also released sets by H. Dockal, O. Kubel, G. Binke and others.

Many of his paintings were created to show the participants dramatizing the tales with the first card as the beginning and the last as the ending. All cards that we have seen are strictly in the German language, but it is very easy to identify each series from the characters displayed. Although not as popular as the beautiful Poster cards of Eric Schutz and E. Kutzer, the works of Oskar Herrfurth are still in great demand.

The Uvachrom Company appeared to be great advertisers. Each separate set or series came with a printed wrapper which listed their complete lineup in a particular motif. An example of this listing with prices and some English titles is shown below.

HERRFURTH, OSKAR (Germany)
   Uvachrom, Stuttgart
   Brothers Grimm Fairy Tales (6 per Series)
   Listing includes sets by several artists.

125 "Hänsel & Gretel"	6 - 8	8 -10
128 "Rotkäppchen"		
(Little Red Riding Hood)	6 - 8	8 - 10
139 "Frau Holle" (Lady Hell)	4 - 6	6 - 8
140 "Dornröschen" (Sleeping Beauty)	6 - 8	8 - 10
147 "Schneewittchen" (Snow White)	6 - 8	8 - 10
154 "Aschenbrödl" (Cinderella)	6 - 8	8 - 10
223 "Der Gestiefelte Kater" (Puss in Boots)	5 - 6	6 - 8
241 "Die Gänsemagd" (The Goose Maid)	5 - 6	6 - 8
242 "Der Rattenfänger von Hameln"		
(Pied Piper of Hamlin)	6 - 8	8 - 10
252 "Der Schweinhirt" (The Pig Herdsman)	5 - 6	6 - 8
254 "Siebenschon"	5 - 6	6 - 8
264 "Der Tannenbaum" (The Fir Tree)	4 - 5	5 - 6
265 "Der Wolf und die Sieben Geisslein"		
(The Wolf and the Seven Goats)	5 - 6	6 - 8
266 "Marienkind"	5 - 6	6 - 8
267 "Tischlein deck dich"	4 - 5	5 - 6
268 "Die Sieben Schwaben"	5 - 6	6 - 8
269 "Brüderchein und Schwesterchen"	6 - 7	7 - 8
285 "Die Bremer Stadtmusikanten"	5 - 6	6 - 8
298 "Hans im Glück"	5 - 8	8 - 10
299 "Das Tapfere Schneiderlein"	5 - 6	6 - 8
311 "Der Kleine Däumling" (Tom Thumb)	6 - 8	8 - 10
319 "Hase und Igel - Das Lumpengesindel"	5 - 6	6 - 8
320 "Die Sieben Raben" (The Seven Ravens)	6 - 8	8 - 10
324 "Münchhausen I"	4 - 5	5 - 6
325 "Münchhausen II"	4 - 5	5 - 6
354 "Das Schlaraffenland"		
(Milk & Honey Land)	4 - 5	5 - 6
355 "Der Frosch König" (The Frog King)	6 - 8	8 - 10
363 "Die Heinselmännchen"	8 - 10	10 - 12
369 "Till Eulenspiegel" (12 cards)	4 - 5	5 - 6
376 "Schneeweifchen und Rosenrot --		
Die Sterntaler"	6 - 7	7 - 8
379 "König Drosselbart"	4 - 5	5 - 6
387 "Caliph Stork"	4 - 5	5 - 6
388 "Aus Flem deutschen Märchenwald I"	4 - 5	5 - 6
406 "Aus Flem deutschen Märchenwald II"	4 - 5	5 - 6
407 "Rumpelstilken"	6 - 8	8 - 10
413 "Märchen-Elfen"	5 - 6	6 - 8

TALES (Sagen) Other than Grimm (6-Card Series)
Sage - A fantastic or incredible tale.

127 "Die Nibelungen - Sage"	8 - 10	10 - 12
141 "Parsival" (Parsifal)	8 - 10	10 - 12
157 "Rübezahl I"	6 - 8	8 - 10
158 "Wilhelm Tell" (12)		
161 "Rübezahl II"		

P.F.B., Series 3714
Cinderella

P.F.B., Series 3714
Hansel & Gretel

P.F.B., Series 3714
Sleeping Beauty

P.F.B., Series 3714
Red Riding Hood

239	"Die Tristan - Sage"	8 - 10	10 - 12
247	"Die Parsival - Sage I"		
253	"Die Parsival - Sage II"		
248	"Walther von der Vogelweide"		
258	"Die Lohengrin - Sage"		
259	"Die Tannhäuser - Sage"		
263	"Aus der Zeit der Minnesänger"		
361	"Der Lichtenstein" (12)		

HEY, PAUL (Germany)
Fairy Tales

"Aschenbrödel"	10 - 12	12 - 15
"Red Riding Hood"		
"Rübezahl"		
"Schneewitchen"		
Others		

HINKLE, G.
Tales

"Hans Im Glück" (6)	8 - 10	10 - 12
Other Series		

HOEST, G. (Germany) — 8 - 10 — 10 - 12

HUTAF, AUGUST W. (U.S.)
Series 105 (Little Bakers)

2089	"Pat-a-Cake"	10 - 12	12 - 15
2090	"Make Me a Cake ..."		
2091	"Criss It and Cross It ..."		
2092	"Put It in the Oven ..."		
2093	"Put on the Chocolate ..."		
2094	"Icing and Candles ..."		

JACKSON, HELEN (G.B.)
Raphael Tuck
Series 6749 "Art" (6)

"I Love Pussy"	18 - 22	22 - 25
"Jack & Jill"		
Others		

JUCHTZER, F. (Germany)

"Rumplestilkin"	8 - 10	10 - 12
Others		

KENNEDY, A. E. (G.B.)
C. W. Faulkner

Series 1633 (6)	12 - 15	15 - 18

KOCH, A. O. (Germany)
Deutsche Märchen

"Ashenbrödel" Cinderella	15 - 18	18 - 22
"Hansel and Gretel"		

KUBEL, OTTO (Germany)
Uvachrom, Stuttgart
Brothers Grimm Fairy Tales

"Aschenbrödl" Cinderella (6)	10 - 12	12 - 15

E. Kutzer, Dereines Südmark 147
"Das Tapfere ... Schneiderlein"

E. Kutzer, Dereines Südmark 151
"Rübezahl"

H. Willibeek LeMair, Augener Ltd., "Little Songs of Long Ago"
"Dame get up and bake your pies."

"Rotkäppchen" Red Riding Hood (6)		
"Dornröschen" Sleeping Beauty (6)		
"Hansel and Gretel" (6)		
Many other Sets		
KUDERNY, F. (Austria)	12 - 15	15 - 18
KUTZER, ERNST (Austria)		
Dereines Sudmark Poster Series		
Comical Fairy Tale Series (6)		
147 "Das Tapfere Schneiderlein"	18 - 22	22 - 25
"Der Kleine Däumling"		
"Die Sieben Schwansen"		
"Rattenfänger von Hameln"		
"Der Ritten Blaubart"		
151 "Rübezahl"		
Non-Poster Series (6)		
"Aschenbrödl"	12 - 15	15 - 18
"Das Tapfer Schneiderlein"		
"Die Seben Raben"		
"Rotkäppchen"		
"Schneewitchen"		
Other		
Bund Der Deutschen		
373 "Rotkäppchen" (Red Riding Hood)	18 - 22	22 - 25
375 "Aschenbrödel"		
LANDSTROM, B. (Finland)	6 - 8	8 - 10

H. Willibeek LeMair, Augener Ltd., "Little Songs of Long Ago"
"I saw three ships a sailing."

LeMAIR, WILLIBEEK (G.B.?)
  Augener, Ltd.

Our Old Nursery Rhymes (12)	15 - 18	18 - 22

"Baa Baa Black Sheep"
"Hickory, Dickory, Dock"
"Georgy Porgy"
"Here We Go Round the Mulberry Bush"
"I Love Little Pussy"
"Little Bo Peep"
"Mary Had a Little Lamb"
"Oranges and Lemons"
"O Where is My Little Dog Gone"
"Pat a Cake"
"Pussy Cat, Pussy Cat"
"Sing a Song of Sixpence"

Old Rhymes With New Pictures (12)	12 - 15	15 - 18

"Humpty Dumpty"
"Little Boy Blue"
"Little Miss Muffet"
"Lucy Locket"
"Polly Put the Kettle on ..."
"Twinkle Twinkle"
"Jack & Jill"
"Little Jack Horner"
"Little Mother"
"Mary, Mary ..."

"Robert Barnes, fellow fine,
Can you shoe this horse o' mine?"
"Ay, good Sir, that I can, —
As well as any other man!"

Little Jack Horner
Sat in a corner,
Eating his Christmas pie.
He put in his thumb
And pulled out a plum,
And said "What a good boy am I!"

Little Boy Blue, come blow up your horn,
The sheep's in the meadow, the cow's
in the corn.
And where is the boy who looks after the sheep?
He's under the haycock, fast asleep!

Little Miss Muffet sat on a tuffet
Eating her curds and whey.
There came a great spider, and sat
down beside her
And frightened Miss Muffet away!

To market, to market,
To buy a plum bun,
Home again, home again, —
Marketing's done!

Mary, Mary, quite contrary,
How does your garden grow?
With silver bells and cockle shells,
And pretty maids all in a row!

H.G.C.MARSH-LAMBERT
"NURSERYRHYMES"SERIES550
A.M.DAVIS&COMPANY

(1) "RobertBarnes,fellowfine,..."
(2) "LittleJackHornersatinacorner..."
(3) "LittleBoyBlue,comeblowyourhorn..."
(4) "LittleMissMuffetsatonatuffet..."
(5) "Tomarket,tomarket..."
(6) "Mary,Mary,quitecontrary..."

"Three Blind Mice"
"Yankee Doodle"
Little Songs of Long Ago (12)   12 - 15   15 - 18
"Dame Get Up and Bake Your Pies"
"I Had a Little Nut Tree"
"I Saw Three Ships a Sailing"
"Little Polly Flinders"
"Little Tom Tucker"
"London Bridge Has Broken Down"
"Old King Cole"
"Over the Hills and Far Away"
"There Came to My Window"
"The North Wind Doth Blow"
"Young Lambs to Sell"
"Simple Simon"
Little People (6)   12 - 15   15 - 18
"Evening Prayer"
"In the Garden"
"Good Evening, Mr. Hare"
"Little Culprit"
"In the Belfrey"
"Time to Get Up"
More Old Nursery Rhymes (12)   15 - 18   18 - 22
"A Frog He Would a Wooing Go"
"A Happy Family"
"Bed Time"
"Curley Locks"
"Girls and Boys Come Out to Play"
"Hush-a-by Baby"
"Ride a Cock Horse"
"The Crooked Man"
"There Was a Little Man"
"Three Little Kittens"
Old Dutch Nursery Rhymes   15 - 18   18 - 22
"Follow the Leader"
"Our Baby Prince"
"Polly Perkin"
"The Little Sailor"
"The Marionettes"
"The Tiny Man"
"Turn Round, Turn Round"
Small Rhymes for Small People   12 - 15   15 - 18
"Dance-a-Baby Ditty"
"Dance to Your Daddy"
"Goosey Gander"
"Lavender Blue"
"Lazy Sheep"
"Little Jumping Joan"

JACK AND JILL.

Jack and Jill went up the hill | Jack fell down and broke his crown,
To fetch a pail of water, | And Jill came tumbling after.

Hilda T. Miller, C. W. Faulkner 1784
"Jack and Jill ..."

"Sleep, Baby, Sleep"
"The Babes in the Woods"
"Three Mice Went to a Hole to Spin"
M.M.H. (G.B.)
  Newman, Wolsey & Co.
    Nursery Rhymes   10 - 12   12 - 15
MARSH-LAMBERT, H.G.C. (G.B.)
  A. M. Davis & Co.
    Nursery Rhymes Series 518 (6)
    "Hush Baby my dolly ..."   20 - 22   22 - 25
    "I had a little hobby-horse ..."
    "Little Bo-Peep ..."
    "Mary had a little lamb ..."
    "Multiplication is vexation ..."
    "Tom, Tom, the Piper's son ..."
    Nursery Rhymes Series 550 (6)
    "Robert Barnes, fellow fine ..."   20 - 25   25 - 28
    "Little Jack Horner ..."
    "Little Boy Blue ..."
    "Little Miss Muffet ..."
    "To Market, to market ..."
    "Mary, Mary, quite contrary..."
MILLAIS, J. E. (G.B.)
    "The Knight Errant" (Tales)   10 - 12   12 - 15
MILLER, HILDA T. (G.B.)
  C. W. Faulkner & Sons

*H. Pinggera, Bund der Deutschen
246, "Rübezahl"*

*Agnes Richardson, R. Tuck C1422
"The Goose Girl"*

Series 1746 Fairy Tales		
"Snowdrop"	15 - 20	20 - 25
"Snow-White and Rose Red"		
Series 1784 Nursery Rhymes		
"See-Saw, Margery Daw"	15 - 20	20 - 25
"Tom was a Piper's Son"		
MILLER, MARION (U.S.)		
Ernest Nister		
Series 2032		
"I saw Three Ships come sailing..."	12 - 15	15 - 18
MUHLBERG, GEORG (Germany)	8 - 10	10 - 12
NICKLASS, LOTTE (Germany)		
"Märchen" Series 3 Silhouettes		
"Thousand & One Nights" (6)	12 - 15	15 - 18
NIXON, K. (G.B.)		
C. W. Faulkner & Co.		
"Alice in Wonderland" (6)	15 - 18	18 - 22
NOSWORTHY, FLORENCE E. (U.S.)		
F. A. Owen, Series 160	10 - 12	12 - 14
NYSTROM, JENNY (Sweden)		
Anon. Publisher (Rooster)		
Series 502 Signed and Unsigned		
7224 "Cinderella"	20 - 22	22 - 25
7225 "Snow White"		

7226 "Sleeping Beauty"
"Red Riding Hood"
"Hansel & Gretel"
Others

Axel Eliason, Stockholm

"Red Riding Hood"	20 - 22	22 - 25
"Hansel and Gretel"		
Other Signed Issues		
Unsigned Issues	10 - 12	12 - 14

H.P. (Austria)

Deutschen Schulverein

Poster

61 "Rübezahl"	15 - 18	18 - 22

PAYER, E. (Germany)

P.G.W.I.

"Der Froschkönig"	12 - 15	15 - 18

V.S.M.

The Frog King (Untitled)	15 - 18	18 - 22

PEZELLERZ, F. (Germany)

Silhouette Fairy Tales

"Der Rattenfänger of Hameln"	12 - 15	15 - 18
"Hansel & Gretel"		

PINGGERA, HEINZ (Austria)

Bund der Deutschen in Niederösterreich

Posters

239 "Sans Däumling" (Tom Thumb)	22 - 25	25 - 28
240 "Schneewittchen" (Snow White)		
241 "Das Tapfere Schneiderlein und die Riefen"		
242 "Siegfried"		
243 "Frauhitt"		
245 "Aschenpuitel" (Cinderella)		
246 "Rübezahl"		
248 "Herr Olof"		
249 "Parsifal"		
250 "Tannhäuser"		
251 "Jung Frau"		
Others		

ROWLAND, FR. (Germany)

"Rübezahl"	12 - 15	15 - 18
Others		

RYAN, C. (U.S.)	10 - 12	12 - 15
SCHIRMER, ANNA (Germany)	8 - 10	10 - 12

SCHUTZ, ERIC (Austria)

B.K.W.I.

Poster Cards

Series 435 (6) Andersen's Fairy Tales	25 - 30	30 - 35
1		
2 "Der König und de Prinzessin"		

E. Schutz, Schulverein 321
"Rotküppchen"

E. Schutz, Schulverein 322
"Die 7 Raben"

E. Schutz, Schulverein 319
"Rumpelstilschen"

E. Schutz, B.K.W.I. 885-3
"Der Rattenfänger" (Pied Piper)

M. Sowerby, Humphrey Milford
"Beauty and the Beast"

M. Sowerby, Humphrey Milford
"Goldilocks"

M. Sowerby, Humphrey Milford
"Little Jack Horner"

M. Sowerby, Humphrey Milford
"Little Bo Peep"

M. Sowerby, Humphrey Milford
"Cinderella"

M. Sowerby, Humphrey Milford
"Little Miss Muffet"

M. Sowerby, Humphrey Milford
"Tom, the Piper's Son"

M. Sowerby, Humphrey Milford
"Little Boy Blue"

The Sleeping Beauty and the Prince.

Cinderella and her Sisters.

L. Wain, R. Tuck "Calendar" 304
"The Sleeping Beauty and the..."

L. Wain, R. Tuck "Calendar" 304
"Cinderella and her Sisters."

   3 "Das kleine Däumelieschen"
   4 "Märchen von der Prinzessin..."
   5 Andersens Märchen "Elfenbügel"
   6 "Die Princessin un der Schweinehirt"
Series 885 (6)
Poster Cards of Fairy Tales   25 - 30   30 - 35
   1
   2 Göthe - "Der Gott und die Baiadere"
   3 Göthe - "Der Rattenfänger" Pied Piper
   4 Göthe - "Der Zauberlchrung"
   5
   6 Göthe - "Hochzeitlied"
Deutscher Schulverein
Poster Cards of Fairy Tales
319 "Rumpelstilzchen"   25 - 30   30 - 35
320 "Schneewittchen" (Snow White)
321 "Rotkäppchen" (Red Riding Hood)
322 "Die Sieben Raben" (Seven Ravens)
564 "Aschenbrödel" (Cinderella)
591 "Das tapfere Schneiderlein"
653 "Der Froschkönig" (The Frog King)
654 "Dornröschen" (Sleeping Beauty)
862 "Dornröschen" (Sleeping Beauty)
SOWERBY, AMY MILLICENT (G.B.)

Louis Wain, Raphael Tuck's "Paper Doll Cats" Series 3385
"Dick Whittington and his Cat"

Humphrey Milford, London
   "Favourite Nursery Rhymes" (6)

"Little Bo-Peep"	25 - 30	30 - 35

     "Little Jack Horner"
     "Little Miss Muffet"
     "Mistress Mary"
     "The Piper's Son"
     "Wee Willie Winkle"
   "Favourite Nursery Stories" (6)

"The Babes in the Wood"	25 - 30	30 - 35

     "Beauty and the Beast"
     "Cinderella"
     "Goldilocks"
     "Jack and the Beanstalk"
     "Red Riding Hood"
   "Storyland Children" (6)

"Little Boy Blue"	25 - 30	30 - 35

     "Little Bo-Peep"
     "Little Miss Muffet"
     "Red Riding Hood"
     "Tom, the Piper's Son"

SPURGIN, FRED (Latvia)
  R. Tuck

Series 3032 "In Fairyland" (6)	15 - 18	18 - 22

TARRANT, MARGARET (G.B.)
  T. P. & Company, N.Y.

"Story Book Series"	6 - 8	8 - 10

  TYPO, Boston

"Tell Me a Story"	6 - 8	8 - 10
Valentine's Series (6)	6 - 8	8 - 10

THIELE, ARTH. (Germany)

Series 1180 (6)	20 - 25	25 - 28

THOMAS, VICTOR (Germany)
  Hubert Kohler, München
   Deutsche Märchen Series

"Dornröschen"	15 - 18	18 - 22

   Others

WAIN, LOUIS (G.B.)
  Raphael Tuck
   "Calendar" Series 304 (6)

"Cinderella and her Sisters"	100 - 125	125 - 150

     "Little Red Riding Hood" (See Front Cover)
     "The Sleeping Beauty and the Prince"
   "Oilette" Series 3385
   "Paper Doll Cats" (6)

"Aladdin"	300 - 400	400 - 600

     "Beauty and the Beast"
     "Cinderella"

Flora White, Salmon Ltd. 1915
"Red Riding Hood"

Flora White, Salmon Ltd. 1470
"Cinderella"

Flora White, Salmon Ltd. 1779
"Jack and the Beanstalk"

Flora White, Salmon Ltd. 1469
"Babes in the Wood"

"Little Red Riding Hood"		
"Robinhood"		
"Dick Whittington"	350 - 400	400 - 450

WALL, BERNHARDT (U.S.)

Ullman Mfg. Co.

"Nursery Rhymes" Series 1664-1669

1664 "Little Bo Peep..."	15 - 18	18 - 22
1665 "To market, to market..."		
1666 "Rain, rain go away..."		
1667 "See saw, Marjorie Daw..."		
1668 "Goosey, Goosey, Gander..."		
1669 "Come, let's go to bed..."		
"Red Riding Hood" Series	15 - 18	18 - 22
1752 "Take Some Cakes ..."		
1753 "On the Way to Grandmother's ..."		
1754 "Arrives at Grandmother's ..."		
1755 "Comes to Bed ..."		
1756 "Innocently Lay Down in Bed ..."		
1757 "Hears the Wolf Say ..."		
"Mary and Her Lamb" Series 1759-1762	12 - 15	15 - 18

WEISLEIN (Germany)

638 "Aschenbrödel"	12 - 15	15 - 18
"Barbarossa"	10 - 12	12 - 15

WHEELER, DOROTHY (G.B.)

Humphrey Milford

"Snow Children" Series (6)	12 - 15	15 - 20

WHITE, FLORA (G.B.)

Ilfracombe Mermaid, "Who are You?"	20 - 25	25 - 30
J. Salmon Poster Series	10 - 12	12 - 15
"Cinderella"		
"Dick Whittington"		
"Goose Girl"		
"Hop-O-My-Thumb"		
"Peter Pan"		
"Puss 'n' Boots"		

WILKE "Bear in Tree" Series	8 - 10	10 - 12

WINKLER, ROLF (Germany)

Anonymous

Paper Doll Cutouts

Series 3382 "Little Bo-Peep"	50 - 60	60 - 70
Series 3383 "Little Boy Blue"	50 - 60	60 - 70

PUBLISHERS

Julius Bien

Series 40 Nursery Rhymes (6)	10 - 12	12 - 15

A. & C. Black

Series 44, 45 (6) "English Nursery Rhymes"	12 - 15	15 - 18

Anonymous, L&GD
"Rotkäppchen"

Series 80 "Alice in Wonderland"	20 - 25	25 - 28
Clark, C. S., Series 2	8 - 10	10 - 12
Axel Eliassons, Stockholm (See Jenny Nystrom)		
F.A.S. Co., Series 9 (6)	8 - 10	10 - 12
Fairman Co. Series 625 B&W	8 - 10	10 - 12
Finkenrath, Paul (P.F.B.)		
Series 3714 (6)		
"Cinderella"	25 - 30	30 - 35
"The House of Sweets"		
"Little Red Riding Hood"		
"Sleeping Beauty"		
"Snow White"		
"Tom Thumb"		
Series 6943 (6)	22 - 25	25 - 28
Series 8666 (6)		
"Cinderella"	25 - 30	30 - 35
"The House of Sweets"		
"Little Red Riding Hood"		
"Sleeping Beauty"		
"Snow White"		
"Tom Thumb"		
Others		
F. Firth & Co. Rhymes	8 - 10	10 - 12
German-American Novelty Art		
Series 307 Fairy Tales (6)	12 - 15	15 - 18
Series 397 Fairy Tales (6)		
Gottschalk & Dreyfuss (German)		

Series 2114 (6) Nursery Rhymes	10 - 12	12 - 15
Series 2115 (6) Nursery Rhymes		
W. & A. K. Johnston		
Series B1 (6)	8 - 10	10 - 12
Vivian A. Mansell & Co., London		
Series 1057 (6)	10 - 12	12 - 15
Series 2105 (6)	8 - 10	10 - 12
Misch & Stock		
Series 120 (6)		
"Fairy Tales & Pantomimes"	10 - 12	12 - 15
National Art Company		
Series 308 - 314 (6)	10 - 12	12 - 15
F. A. Owen		
Series 160 (6)	8 - 10	10 - 12
Series 161 (6)		
Rooster Trademark		
Series 502	10 - 12	12 - 15
Salmon & Company		
Fairy Tale Series	10 - 12	12 - 15
Tuck, Raphael		
Ser. IX Glosso **"Happy Childhood"** (B&W)	6 - 8	8 - 10
Series 9		
"Little Nursery Lovers" (12) Red Border		
"Taffy was a Welshman..."	12 - 15	15 - 18
Others		
Series 12		
"Nursery Don'ts" (12) Green Border		
"Don't be cruel to dumb animals"	12 - 15	15 - 18
"Don't be late for school"		
"Don't be stingy"		
"Don't count your chickens before..."		
"Don't criticize your friends"		
"Don't cry over spilled milk"		
"Don't drive a willing horse to death"		
"Don't forget to cross your T's & dot your I's"		
"Don't give up the ship"		
"Don't let the cat out of the bag"		
"Don't put off till tomorrow..."		
"Don't trouble trouble til trouble..."		
Series 132 "Lovers in Nurseryland" (6)	12 - 15	15 - 18
Series 3376 "Nursery Rhymes" (6)	10 - 12	12 - 18
Series 3328, 3379, 3488 (6)	10 - 12	12 - 18
Series 3470-3475 (6) Chromolithographs		
"Cinderella"	20 - 25	25 - 30
"Puss 'n' Boots"		
"Red Riding Hood"		
"Sleeping Beauty"		
"Snow White"		

"Tom Thumb"

Series 132 "Lovers in Nursery Land" (6)	8 - 10	10 - 12
Series 5579 "Happy Childhood"	8 - 10	10 - 12
Series 5600 "Cat Studies" (6) (B&W)	12 - 15	15 - 18
Series 5629 "Pussy in Fairyland"	10 - 12	12 - 14
Series 6496 "Landor's Cat Studies" (B&W)	6 - 8	8 - 10

T. P. & Co., New York

"Story Book" Series

"Dick Whittington"	10 - 12	12 - 15

"Red Riding Hood"

Others

Tullar-Meredith

"Three Little Pigs" (5)	10 - 12	12 - 15

Ullman Mfg. Co.

See Bernhardt Wall

ANONYMOUS

Eagle on back Series, Lacy Border (10)

"Cock-a doodle-doo..."	10 - 12	12 - 15

"Little Bo Peep has lost her sheep..."

"Little Boy Blue..."

"Little Jack Horner..."

"Mary, Mary, quite contrary..."

"Old Mother Hubbard"

"Pussy Cat, Pussy Cat..."

ADVERTISING

Dr. Swett's Root Beer

Nursery Rhymes

"Jack Spratt"	25 - 30	30 - 35

"Little Jack Horner"

Fralinger's Original Salt Water Taffy (24)	25 - 30	30 - 35

See **C. M. Burd**

Minneapolis Knitting

Nursery Rhymes (6)	15 - 20	20 - 25

"Baa Baa Black Sheep..."

"Jack and Jill..."

"Mary had a little lamb..."

"Pat a cake, pat a cake..."

"Pussy Cat, Pussy Cat..."

"There was an Old Woman who lived..."

Swift's Premium, 1918

Nursery Rhymes (6)

1 Queen of Hearts	15 - 18	18 - 22

2 Old King Cole

3 Little Jack Horner

4 Little Tommy Tucker

5 Jack Spratt

6 Simple Simon

Louis Wain, R. Tuck Series 8613, "Taking the Harrogate Waters"
"Getting ready for the Sulphurers"

Chapter 4

Dressed Animals

Dressed Animals, or "Animals doing people things," are the overwhelming group of choice for a large contingent of collectors who pursue quality fantasy cards. Many of the early Artist-drawn cards, especially those that are so much in demand today, were adapted from books for children which were published during the 1890 to 1910 era. Artists and publishers of these books took full advantage of the popularity of the postcard by reproducing choice illustrations into selected sets and series for worldwide distribution.

The name of one of the most prominent of these artists, G. H. Thompson, who rarely ever signed his works (and then only with "G.T.") was recently identified by John and Sandy Millns from books mentioned later in the text. Thompson's work for publishers E. Nister and Theo. Stroefer are among today's most revered. In addition to Thompson, Louis Wain has to be another favorite. His cat cards, as well as dogs and other animals, have always been most desirable. Wain's cat Santa cards, those portraying a likeness of Charlie Chaplin, and his fairy tale Paper doll cutout cards are all valued up to $400 or more. He also had some early books on animals.

Another terrific painter of dressed animals was German artist Arth. Thiele. Although most of his work is great, his renditions of large figure cat ladies and children are outstanding. Thiele also produced sets and series of other animals which are in great demand. His cards are usually priced in the $20 to $40 range and many are considered to be undervalued in today's ever expanding market.

DRESSED ANIMALS, INSECTS, BIRDS

SECTION I. ANIMALS, MIXED

This section is composed of sets or series, by artists or publishers, where a group of different animals appear on the same card or where all cards in each set portray different animals.

CADY, HARRISON (U.S.)
    "Quaddy" Postcards (10)
    Quaddy Plaything Co.
       "Danny Meadow Mouse" $ 90 - 100 $ 100 - 125
       "Grandfather Frog"
       "Hooty the Owl"
       "Happy Jack Squirrel"
       "Mrs. Peter Rabbit"
       "Peter Rabbit"
       "Reddy Fox"
       "Sammy Jay"
       "Spotty Turtle"
       "Unc' Billy Possum"
DOD, GIL (G.B.)
    S. Hildesheimer
    Series 5244 "Sports Meet" (6)
       Obstacle Race   20 - 25   25 - 28

STEEPLE CHASE

Gil Dod, S. Hildesheimer, Sports Meet Series 5244
"Steeple Chase"

W. Ellam, R. Tuck 9953
"Breakfast in Bed" II

W. Ellam, R. Tuck 9953
"Breakfast in Bed" II

W. Ellam, R. Tuck 9953
"Breakfast in Bed" III

W. Ellam, R. Tuck 9953
"Breakfast in Bed" III

Steeple Chase
Others
ELLAM, WILLIAM HENRY (G.B.)
  Raphael Tuck
    "Breakfast in Bed" I
    Series 9321 (6)
    Chickens   20 - 22   22 - 25
    Geese
    Donkeys
    Others
    Series II
    Elephants
    Bears
    Bunnies
    Others
    "Breakfast in Bed" III   Series 9953 (6)
    Bulldogs
    Deer
    Monkeys
    Parrots
    Others
    "Breakfast in Bed" IV   Series 9784 (6)
    Zebras
    "Breakfast in Bed"   Series 9793 (6)

Bears
Lions
Pigs
Zebras

Series 574B German Captions (6)	15 - 18	18 - 22

"Mixed Bathing" Series 9562 (6)
Elephants
Frogs
Others
"Mrs. Caudle's Curtain Lectures"
Series 8683

Cats	18 - 22	22 - 25

Chickens
Collie Dogs
Donkeys
Ducks
Geese
Series II 8684 (6)

Parrots	15 - 18	18 - 22

Others
GRATZ, THOMAS (Germany)
    Fingerie & Co.

Dressed Animals	10 - 12	12 - 15

G. H. THOMPSON

The name of G. H. Thompson should be synonymous with classical dressed animals on postcards. The lovable wild animal works he did for publisher E. Nister of London, and printed by accomplished German craftsmen, are truly works of art. One of his wonderful books, *The Animals' Trip to Sea,* was published by E. Nister and distributed in the U.S. by E. P. Dutton & Co., New York. It told the story of a large group of dressed wild animals on an adventurous sea voyage. The great illustrations show in detail the humorous happenings of a group that were decidedly out of their natural habitat.

From illustrations in this book Nister published **Series 179**, a series of six postcards entitled **"The Animals' Trip to Sea."** Each colorful card shows groupings of animals at particular points in the story. Nister, and later publisher Theo. Stroefer, Nürnberg (T.S.N.), selected animals from these smaller images and enlarged them to form sets and series such as **Series 70** and **T.S.N. Series 319,** etc. These unbelievable images of lovable rhinos, hippos, elephants, lions, etc., are among the most desirable of all Fantasy postcards. Nister and Thompson also combined for at least three other great

Unsigned G.H.T., E. Nister Series 180
"The Animals' Picnic" -- "The Photographer"

Unsigned G.H.T., E. Nister Series 179
"The Animals' Trip to Sea" -- "The Packing"

Many of the dressed animals shown on the above cards, and others in each series, were selected by publishers E. Nister and Theo. Stroefer to be the dominant figure on their own card in later sets and series. The images were enlarged and placed on fabric or sackcloth backgrounds for a more formidable effect. The resulting sets and series are among the most delightful of all dressed animal postcards.

dressed wild animal series. **Series 180, "The Animals' Picnic," Series 181, "The Animals' Rebellion," and Series 354, "The Animals' School,"** all have six cards in each set. Although unproven, it is a distinct possibility that these images were also taken from books by Thompson and Nister. Larger images of animals in these three additional postcard series were also created to form other series listed herein. Collectors who are familiar with the dressed animals of G. H. Thompson have placed them at the very top of their want lists. His works are scarce and very collectible, and the prices have risen accordingly.

G.H.T. (G. H. THOMPSON) (G.B.)
    Ernest Nister, London
        "The Animals Trip to Sea"
        Series 179 (6) (Signed/Uns. G.H.T.)
        "The Accident"   40 - 50   50 - 60
        "A Rough Sea"
        "Mixed Bathing"
        "The Packing"
        "The Ticket Office"
        "On the Beach"

Unsigned G.H.T.
Theo. Stroefer, Humor Ser. 319-3,

Unsigned G.H.T., E. Nister
Series 70, Rhino in School

Unsigned G.H.T., E. Nister
Series 70, Hippo at Picnic

Unsigned G.H.T., Theo. Stroefer
Series 441-1, Hippo Family

Unsigned G.H.T., T. Stroefer
Series 441-2, Hippo Mother & Son

Unsigned G.H.T., E. Nister
Ser. 70, Hippo w/Bathing Trunks

Unsigned G.H.T., E. Nister, Series 354
"The Animals' School."

"The Animals' Picnic"
Series 180 (6) (Signed/Uns. G.H.T.)
"The Fortune Teller" 40 - 50 50 - 60
"Lunch in the Forest"
"The Moonlight Ball"
"The Photographer"
"Sending the Invitation"
"The Animals' Rebellion"
Series 181 (6) (Uns. G.H.T.)
"The Petition Refused" 40 - 50 50 - 60
"Preparing for the Fray"
"Raising the Standard of Revolt"
"The Rebels Surrender"
"The Triumphal Return"
"The Wounded Hero"
Series 70 (**6**) (Uns. G.H.T.)
Series 172 (6) Hippo Head Series
  Signed GHT
  No. 1 "Eh! What?" 40 - 50 50 - 60
  No. 2 "Would I like a BUN?"
  No. 3 "Chuck it here"
  No. 4 "Thanks"
  No. 5 "That bun was STALE"
  No. 6 "But I don't mind ANOTHER"
Series 354
"The Animals' School" 40 - 50 50 - 60
Large images made from small images
of Series 179, 180, 181, and 354

A. Jiras, R. Tuck 808
"Flowers for Her"

A. Jiras, R. Tuck 808
Courting Donkeys

The Rhino	40 - 50	50 - 60
The Hippo		
The Hippo with Bathing Trunks		
Others		
Series 316 (Uns. G.H.T.) (6)	35 - 40	40 - 50
Series 328 (Uns. G.H.T.) (6)		
Series 331 (Uns. G.H.T.) (6)		
Series 333 (Uns. G.H.T.) (6)		
T.S.N. (**Theo. Stroefer,** Nürnberg)		
Series 319 (6)		
"Tierpostkarten" (Uns. G.H.T.)		
"Elephant"	35 - 40	40 - 45
Others		
Series 325 "Animals" (Uns. G.H.T.)		
Bear on Bike Chases Pig	30 - 35	35 - 40
Others		
Series 330 (6) (Uns. G.H.T.)		
Bunnies - The Barber	30 - 35	35 - 38
Others		
Series 441 (6) (Uns. G.H.T.)		
Large Images from Small Images **of "The Animals' Picnic"**		
Hippo Family	35 - 40	40 - 45
Mama Hippo and Son		
Others		

Eugen Opswald, Wilh. Stephan Sports Series, "Der Sieger"

Eugen Opswald, Wilh. Stephan Sports Series, "Der Torwart."

C. H. Twelvetrees, Ullman Ser. 77 1893, "Sweet Little Buttercup"

C. H. Twelvetrees, Ullman Ser. 77 1894, "Harry Halfback"

Arth. Thiele, T.S.N. Series 1215
Head Studies

Arth. Thiele, T.S.N. Series 1215
Head Studies

Series 757 (6) (Uns. G.H.T.)
Same series as #79 above "The
Animals Trip to the Sea"   30 - 35   35 - 40
Series 965 (6) (Uns. G.H.T.)
"Motoring" Series (6)   25 - 28   28 - 32
JIRAS, A. (Austria?)
Monopol, Austria
Series 220 (6)
Various animal couples   25 - 30   30 - 35
R. Tuck
Series 808 Love and Marriage Series (6)
"Flowers for Her"   25 - 30   30 - 35
Courting Donkeys
OPSWALD, EUGEN (Germany)
Wilh. Stephan, München
"Animal Sports" Series (6)
"Der Sieger"   35 - 50   50 - 75
"Der Torwart"
Others
ROWNTREE, HARRY (G.B.)
Vivian Mansell & Co.
Series 1077 (6) Various animals   15 - 18   18 - 22
SANCHA, F. (Spain?)
Raphael Tuck
"Aesop's Fables Up to Date" (6)

"The Dog and the Shadow"	20 - 25	25 - 30
"The Fox and the Grapes"		
"The Hare and the Tortoise"		
"The Hen that laid the Golden egg"		
"The Tortoise and the Eagle"		
"The Wolf and the Stork"		

STANTON, CHARLES R. (G.B.)
  C. W. Faulkner & Co.

Fantasy Animals Series 1127 (6)		
"The Bejangerweasel"	20 - 25	25 - 30
"The Flooten Pusher"		
"The Ifflesoffleisafossil"		
"The Jacko-Mackacko"		
"The Ooflepiffle"		
Other		

THIELE, ARTH. (Germany)
  T.S.N.

Series 1215 Horse Head Studies (6)	30 - 35	35 - 40
Series 1413 Animal Head Studies (6)	22 - 25	25 - 30

TWELVETREES, CHARLES H. (U.S.)
  Ullman Mfg. Co.

Jungle Sports Series 77		
1893 Hippo - "Sweet Little Butterfly"	18 - 22	22 - 25
1894 Elephant - "Harry Halfback"		
1895 Giraffe plays golf - "On the Job"	22 - 25	25 - 28
1896 Stork - "The Last Pebble on the..."	18 - 22	22 - 25

PUBLISHERS

Ullman Mfg. Co.		
"Jungle Sports" Series 72	15 - 18	18 - 22

SECTION II -- ANIMALS, SPECIFIC

BEARS (Also see Teddy Bear Section)

BAUMGARTEN, FRITZ (F.B.)		
Oppel and Hess		
Series 1457, 1458, 1486 and 1511	12 - 15	15 - 20
CHARLIN, F.	12 - 15	15 - 18
ELLAM, WILLIAM HENRY (G.B.)		
Raphael Tuck		
Series II 9553 (1)	20 - 25	25 - 28
F.D.S.	15 - 18	18 - 22
FEIERTAG, K. (Austria)		
B.K.W.I.		
Series 160 (6)	12 - 15	15 - 18
GLEISSENBERGER, KARL (Germany)	10 - 12	12 - 15

Unsigned, Novitas 80607
"Fröhliche Pfingsten!"

Nash Easter Series 37
"Easter Joys"

F.B. (Fritz Baumgarten)
Meissner & Buch

GHT (unsigned), Nister Ser. 330
Bunny Series, "The Barber"

D.R.G.M. 88077
Chromolithograph

MANASSE, A. (Austria?)	10 - 12	12 - 15
MARTIN, L. (G.B.)		
OSTERMANN, F. (Germany)		
VON REISEN, A. (Germany)		
TEMPEST, MARGARET (G.B.)		
Medici Society		
Series 61 (6)	8 - 10	10 - 12
PUBLISHERS		
M. Munk, Vienna	12 - 15	15 - 18
S.W.S.B., Series 8837		

BIRDS

OHLER, C. (Hungary)		
The Bird Musicians Series (4)	6 - 8	8 - 10
ORENS, D. (France)		
E.L.D.		
9017 Birds on Mushroom	6 - 8	8 - 10
B.K.W.I. Series 552		
Anonymous		
Others		
Novitas		
80607 Courting Birds		

Arth. Thiele, T.S.N. 1240
Easter Greeting

Lucy, Anon., Animaux Parisiens
"Le Chameau ... Le Daim"

BUNNIES

BAUMGARTEN, FRITZ **(F.B.)** (Germany)
  Meissner & Buch
    Various Series   12 - 15   15 - 20
COBBE, BERNHARD (G.B.)
  Raphael Tuck
    Series 9539 (6)   8 - 10   10 - 12
    Others
DOVIE, E. H. (G.B.)
  Valentine's
    Bunny Series (6)   8 - 10   10 - 12
    Others
ONSLOW, LOLA (G.B.)
  Mack Co.
    "Storybook" Series (6)   8 - 10   10 - 12
THIELE, ARTH. (Germany)
  T.S.N.
    Series 1020 (6) Bunny Family   15 - 20   20 - 25
    Series 1021 (6) Bunny Family
    Series 1240 (6)   20 - 22   22 - 25
    Series 1355 (6)   15 - 18   18 - 22
    Series 1451 (6)   18 - 22   22 - 25
    Others

GHT (Unsigned)
  E. Nister
    Series 330 "Bunny Series"
      "The Barber"   30 - 35   35 - 40

PUBLISHERS

  AMAG, **Series 2143** (6)   12 - 15   15 - 18
  Meissner & Buch, **Series 2960** (6)   15 - 18   18 - 22
  M. Munk, **Series 729** (6)   12 - 15   15 - 18
  Ullman Mfg. Co.
    "Br'er Rabbit" Series 112   12 - 15   15 - 18
    "Bunny Girl" Series 84   10 - 12   12 - 15
    Series 2, 9553-1   8 - 10   10 - 12
  Others
Hold-To-Light   (See H-T-L Section)

CAMELS

LUCE, A. (France)
  Anonymous, Animaux Parisiens
    "Le Chameau...Le Daim"   15 - 20   20 - 25

Louis Wain, R. Tuck No No.
"Jappy and Happy"

Louis Wain, R. Tuck 8615
"I say! Stop it!!"

Louis Wain, R. Tuck 8613
"Between Drinks"

Louis Wain, R. Tuck 3553
"The Skipping Mascot"

Louis Wain, R. Tuck 3551
"The Dandy's Mascot"

Louis Wain, R. Tuck 3551
"The Dancer's Mascot"

Louis Wain, R. Tuck 3553
"The Runner's Mascot"

CATS

BARNES, G. L. (G.B.) (See Nursery Rhymes)	10 - 15	15 - 18
BOULANGER, MAURICE (France)		
H & M Co.		
Series 104 (12) "In Catland" (non-color)	12 - 15	15 - 18
International Art Pub. Co.		
Series 472 (6)	20 - 25	25 - 28
K. F. Editeurs, Paris		
"Chestnuts"	22 - 25	25 - 28
"Confetti"		
"Dinner Time"		
"Merry Days"		
"Shopping"		
"Splashing"		
Raphael Tuck		
Series 122 "Humorous Cats" (6)	25 - 30	30 - 35
Same images as **K. F. Editeurs** set. (6)	22 - 25	25 - 30
"Months of the Year" Series (12)	30 - 35	35 - 40
Series 6878 "Humorous Cats" (6)		
Anonymous		
Series 417 (12) Chromolithos	30 - 35	35 - 40

Louis Wain, R. Tuck 8612
"Down it!"

Louis Wain, R. Tuck 8613
"A Perfect Cure"

C.W. Series 99 (6)	8 - 10	10 - 12
CLIVETTE		
Embossed Series 619 (6) Dancing Cats	12 - 15	15 - 18
MAINZER, ALFRED		
Dressed cats doing people things (40's-60's)	5 - 6	6 - 8
Golf	10 - 12	12 - 15
Tennis	8 - 10	10 - 12
SCHROPLER, L. (Germany)		
A.S.M., Series 625 Dressed Cats (6)	15 - 18	18 - 22
THIELE, ARTH. (Germany)		
F.E.D.		
Series 160 Wash days	20 - 25	25 - 28
Series 474 Cats dancing with T. Bear, etc.		
T.S.N.		
Series 710 Large Cat Heads (6)	25 - 30	30 - 35
Series 861 Large Lady and Girls (6)		
Series 962 Cats in School (6)	15 - 20	20 - 25
Series 947 Diabolo (6)	30 - 35	35 - 40
Series 962 In School (6)	15 - 20	20 - 25
Series 975 Cats at play (6)		
Series 995 Cupid (6)	30 - 35	35 - 40
Series 1010 Little Cats at play (6)	20 - 25	25 - 28
Series 1012 Playing and singing (6)	15 - 20	20 - 25
Series 1077 Washing and housework (6)		
Series 1194 Children at winter play (6)		
Series 1229 Dancing Cats (6)	22 - 25	25 - 28
Series 1326 Mama and kids in kitchen (6)	15 - 20	20 - 25
Series 1405 Playing and singing (6)		
Series 1412 Large Image Kittens (6)		
Cat with bow and arrow	30 - 35	35 - 40
Cat with gun and sword		
Cat with dog and ball		
Series 1423 Cats in gym (6)	15 - 18	18 - 22
Series 1403 Cats in snow (6)	18 - 22	22 - 25
Series 1405 Playing and singing (6)	15 - 18	18 - 22
Series 1423 Learning house duties (6)		
"Big Head, Destructive Kitty"		
Series 1424 (6)		
A Full Pocketbook	30 - 35	35 - 40
Dolly's Bath		
Cleaning up the Mess		
Ink is Very Messy		
Time for Bed		
Using Her Scissors		
Series 1438 Little Kittens (6)	15 - 20	20 - 25
Series 1468 Beautifully Dressed Ladies (6)	30 - 35	35 - 40
Series 1601 The fun Outing (6)	15 - 20	20 - 25
Series 1602 Cats at Market (6)		
Series 1646 The Broken Doll (6)		

Anonymous, Novitas 80-060
"Joyeuses Paques"

Anonymous
Hand-Made

C.L., J. W. & Co. 431
No Caption

Anonymous, Novitas 80610
"Fröliche

Anonymous
Foreign Caption

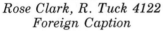

Rose Clark, R. Tuck 4122
Foreign Caption

Rose Clark, R. Tuck 36
"Easter Greetings"

Series 1852 Playing and singing (6)		
Series 1880 In the classroom (6)		
Series 1881 At the market (6)		
Series 1882 Mama and the kids (6)	15 - 20	20 - 25
Series 3575 In the schoolroom (6)		
WAIN, LOUIS (G.B.)		
Max Ettlinger		
Series 5376 Cat Santas	400 - 450	450 - 500
R. Tuck		
Series 3551, "Mascots" (6)		
"The Dancer's Mascot"	150 - 175	175 - 200
"The Contented Mascot"		
"The Dandy's Mascot"		
"The Book"		
"The Dreamland"		
"The Twin Mascots"		
Series 3552, "Mascots" (6)		
"The Doctors"		
"The Huntsmen"		
"The Lucky Day"		
"The Play-Time"		
"The Talkers"		
"The Visitors"		
Series 3553, "Mascots" (6)		
"The Runner's Mascot"		

Louis Wain, R. Tuck 3552
"The Huntsman's Mascot"

Louis Wain, Anonymous
No Caption

Louis Wain, R. Tuck 3552
"The Talker's Mascot"

A. Müller, Erika 3708
No Caption

K. Feiertag, B.K.W.I. 47-2
"Off zum Weekend"

"The Skipping Mascot"
Series 3554, "Mascots" (6)
Series 8612, "Taking the Waters" (6)   100 - 125   125 - 150
"Down it!"
"Here's Health!"
Series 8613, "Taking the Harrogate Waters"
"A Perfect Cure"   100 - 125   125 - 150
"Between Drinks"
Series 8614, "Taking the Harrogate Waters"
"I Don't Think"   100 - 125   125 - 150
"Perhaps if I hold my nose it will go..."
"Oh that this too, too solid flesh ..."
Series 8615, "Taking the Waters"
"I say! Stop it!!"
No No. "Louis Wain Cats"   70 - 80   80 - 90
"Jappy and Happy"
"Charlie Chaplin" Series (6)   250 - 275   275 - 300
Other Series   35 - 50   50 - 75
See Fairy Tales and Santa Sections

PUBLISHERS
Albert Hahn, 1907 "Kaatskill Cats"   10 - 12   12 - 15

CHICKENS, CHICKS

CLARK, ROSE
National Art Co., 102 "Spring Chicken"   12 - 15   15 - 18
R. Tuck
    Series 36 (6)   15 - 18   18 - 22
    Series 4121 (6)
    Series 4122 (6) (French Captions)
THIELE, ARTH. (Germany)
T.S.N.
    Series 1021 (6)   15 - 18   18 - 22
    Series 1165 (6)   15 - 20   20 - 25
    Series 1352 (6)   12 - 15   15 - 20
    Series 1452 (6)   15 - 20   20 - 25

PUBLISHERS

Novitas, 80-060 "Joyeuses Paques"   12 - 15   15 - 20
Others   12 - 15   15 - 18
Hold-To-Light (See H-T-L Section)

COWS, BULLS, ETC.

Miscellaneous   10 - 15   15 - 20
Note: Prices reflect value of the artist.)

A. Thiele, TSN 1413
No Caption

Anonymous, PFB Series 3903
"Cake-Walk"

DOGS

BAUMGARTEN, FRITZ or **(F.B.)** (Germany)		
Meissner & Buch		
Various Series	12 - 15	15 - 20
FEIERTAG, KARL (Austria)		
B.K.W.I.		
Series **47-2** "Off zum Weekend"	15 - 18	18 - 22
Dressed or Doing People Things	10 - 12	12 - 15
FREES, H. W.		
Rotograph Co.		
Comic Dressed Dog Photos	8 - 10	10 - 12
GROSSMAN, O. (Germany)	15 - 18	18 - 22
H.R.U.	8 - 10	10 - 12
HANKE, H. or **(H.H.)** (Germany)		
Series **4056** Dressed Dachshunds (6)	15 - 20	20 - 25
Others	12 - 15	15 - 18
KLUGMAYER (Austria)	10 - 12	12 - 15
MAINZER, ALFRED		
Dressed Dogs doing people things (40-60's)	4 - 5	5 - 6
Golf	10 - 12	12 - 15
Tennis	8 - 10	10 - 12
MÜLLER, AUGUSTUS (Germany)		
Series **3908** Bull Dog	15 - 20	20 - 25

H.A.W., M. Munk 487
No Caption

D. P. Crane, ZIM
"Easter Greeting"

Series 3956 Dachshunds (6)	12 - 15	15 - 18
Other Dressed Series		
OHLER, C. (Germany)		
Comical Dogs	12 - 15	15 - 18
P.O.E. (Germany)	12 - 15	15 - 18
PANKRATZ, Comical Dachshunds	10 - 12	12 - 15
QUIDENUS, F. (Germany)	8 - 10	10 - 12
REICHERT, C. (G.B.)	10 - 12	12 - 15
SCHNOPLER, A. (Austria)		
Comical Dachshunds	12 - 15	15 - 18
STUDDY, GEORGE E. (G.B.)		
B.K.W.I. Series (Bonzo)	10 - 12	12 - 15
Tennis & Golf Themes	15 - 20	20 - 25
Valentine's Series (Bonzo)	10 - 12	12 - 15
Tennis & Golf	15 - 20	20 - 25
Non-Bonzo Studdy Cards		
Non-Studdy Bonzo Cards	10 - 12	12 - 15
THIELE, ARTH. (Germany)		
German-American Art		
Series 806 Head Studies Dressed Dogs		
1 Wearing Clown Hat	20 - 25	25 - 30
2 Wearing Top Hat		
3 Wearing Derby Hat		
4 Wearing Light Straw hat		

5 Wearing Big Slouch Hat		
6 Wearing Tasseled Hat		
T.S.N.		
Series 843 (6)	18 - 22	22 - 25
Series 946 (6) Dressed Dachshunds		
GBWV, Series 55 "Der Froschkönig"	10 - 12	12 - 15
WINKLER, ROLF (Germany)		
NPG		
Scotch dressed hunter	20 - 22	22 - 25
Hunter smoking pipe		
Hunter lighting cigar		
Hunter with binoculars		
Hunter with cigarette		
Series 949 Courtship & Marriage		
1 The meeting at the well	20 - 25	25 - 30
2 Courting against the fence		
3 The Proposal		
4 The Marriage		
5 Preparing to go out		
Series 1128 (6)	12 - 15	15 - 18
Series 1893 (6)		
V.O.	12 - 15	15 - 18
WAIN, LOUIS (G.B.)		
R. Tuck		
Series 3552		
"The Doctor's Mascot"	150 - 175	175 - 200
"The Huntsman's Mascot"		
"The Talker's Mascot"		
Others		
Anonymous Old dog with injured foot	50 - 60	60 - 70
PUBLISHERS		
H.H.i.W. Series 459 (6)	12 - 15	15 - 20
P.F.B.		
Series 5957 Embossed (6)	20 - 25	25 - 28
P.F.B.		
Series 8168 Embossed (6)		
Ullman Mfg. Co.		
"Jungle Sports" Series 72	12 - 15	15 - 18
"Monkey Doodle" Series 196	8 -10	10 - 12

DONKEYS

JIRAS, A. (Germany?)		
Raphael Tuck		
Donkey "Love and Marriage"		
Series 808 (6)	20 - 25	25 - 30
Others	10 - 12	12 - 15

Hy-M, Nister 180
"Jumbos Skipping Rope"

Hy-M, Nister 180
"The Jumbo Circus"

Hy-M, Nister 180
"Fisherman's Luck"

Hy-M, Nister 180
"Jumbo's Table Manners"

Hy-M, Nister 180
"Jumbo's Roller Skating"

Hy-M, Nister 180
"On the River"

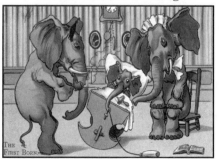

Hy-M, Nister 187-3
"The First Born"

Hy-M, Nister 187-2
"Off to School"

DUCKS

CRANE, D. P. (U.S.)		
ZIM		
Mother with Baby Duckling	20 - 22	22 - 25
GUGGENBERGER, I. G. (Germany)	10 - 12	12 - 15
H.A.W.		
M. Munk		
487 Flying Duck	25 - 30	30 - 35
OHLER, C. (Hungary)		
Series 553 (4)		
Duck Band	8 - 10	10 - 12
See Saw		
Fishing		
To School		
ROWNTREE, HARRY (G.B.)		
British Showcard Poster Co.		
"Sporting Duckling" Series		
"Fishing"	10 - 15	12 - 15
"Hunting"		
"Jumping"		
"Running"		
"Yachting"		

ELEPHANTS

HY-M (Henry Mayer) (Germany)		
E. Nister		
"Jumbo" Series 186 (6) (Uns.)		
1 "The First Meeting"	30 - 35	35 - 40
2 "The Jungle Waltz"		
3 "Strike, Good Luck!"		
4 "Jumbo Diving"		
6 "Young Jumbo's Shower Bath"		
"Jumbo" Series 187 (6)		
1 "Dr. Jumbo and His Pupils"	30 - 35	35 - 40
2 "Off to School"		
3 "The First Born"		
4 "A Loving Embrace"		
5 "Jumbo's Christmas"		
"Jumbo" Elephant Series 188 (6)		
1 "Jumbo's Skipping Rope"	30 - 35	35 - 40
2 "Fisherman's Luck"		
3 "The Jumbo Circus"		
4 "Jumbo's Table Manners"		
5 "Jumbo's Roller Skating"		
6 "On the River"		

Anonymous
"Fish Dancer" Series

Anonymous, French April Fool
"1 er Avril"

Anonymous
"Fish Lovers" Series

Anon., Misch & Co. Series 420
"Fishy Customers"

Anonymous, A.&M.B. 467
No Caption

Anon., Misch & Co. Series 420
"Fishy Customers"

"Jumbo" Elephant Series 189 (6)		
"Jumbo on Exhibition"	30 - 35	35 - 40
"Jumbo on Tour"		
"Look Pleasant Please"		
"The Latest News"		
"Jumbo's Surprise"		
ELLAM, WILLIAM HENRY (G.B.)		
Raphael Tuck		
Series 9684 "Trunks Full of Fun" (6)	25 - 30	30 - 35
Series 9684 Puzzle Postcards (6)	40 - 50	50 - 60
ROGER (France)		
K.F. Editeurs, Paris (Sepia)		
Series 590 (6)		
Elephant in Restaurant	15 - 20	20 - 25

FISH

PUBLISHERS

A. & M. B.		
Series 467 Chromolithos (6)	25 - 30	30 - 35
Misch & Co.		
Series 420 "Fishy Customers" Chromos. (6)	20 - 25	25 - 30
Anonymous		
Fish Lovers Chromolithos	20 - 25	25 - 30
Fish "Dancer" Series	18 - 22	22 - 25
French 1er Avril (April Fool) Chromos.	18 - 22	22 - 25

FOXES

ELLAM, WILLIAM HENRY (G.B.)		
Raphael Tuck		
Series II 9553 "Breakfast in Bed" (1)	15 - 18	18 - 22
Others	12 - 15	15 - 18

FROGS

A.T., Frog Musicians	12 - 15	15 - 20
BECKMAN, JOHANNA (Austria)		
Märchen Series II Silhouettes		
63 "Der Froschkönig"	12 - 15	15 - 20
BROMBERGER (Germany)	15 - 18	18 - 22
BAUMGARTEN, FRITZ or (F.B.)		
Meissner & Buch Various Series	15 - 20	20 - 25
CLARK, ROSE (U.S.)		
Rotograph Company		
F.L. 379 "Officer Stout Frog"	30 - 35	35 - 40

A.&M.B. 457
No Caption

C. Twelvetrees, National Art 140
"The Groom"

A.&M.B. 697
No Caption

Misch & Stock Series 152
"The Frog a-Wooing"

Anonymous, German
"Volkssänger" (Folk Singers)

Humoristlish Postikarten Ser. 30
No Caption

Rose Clark, Rotograph Co. 381
"Will B. Stout Frog"

Rose Clark, Rotograph Co. 388
"Captain Skippin Frog"

Rose Clark, Rotograph Co. 390
"I. M. De Bull Frog"

Rose Clark, Rotograph Co. 385
"Grandmother Bullsie"

F.L. 380 "Dew-Drop Frog"
F.L. 381 "Will B. Stout Frog"
F.L. 382 "Mrs. Hoppin' Frog ..."
F.L. 383 "Leap Frog"
F.L. 384 "Hammersly Frog,
   the 'Village Smith' ..."
F.L. 385 "Grandmother Bullsie"
F.L. 386 "Lily-Pad Frog"
F.L. 387 "Professor Singer Frog"
F.L. 388 "Captain Skippin Frog, of the
   Froghurst Volunteer Hose Co."
F.L. 389 "Brassie Frog"

F.L. 390 "I. M. De Bull Frog"	40 - 45	45 - 50

FIALKOWSKA, WALLY or **WF** (Austria)
  AMV

1512 "Der Froschkönig"	12 - 15	15 - 20

    1513 "Der Froschkönig"

GUGGENBERGER, I. G. (Germany)

Anonymous Chromolithographs	20 - 25	25 - 30

HERRFURTH, OSKAR & OH (Germany)
  Uvachrom   "Bruder Grimm"

"Der Froschkönig" (6)	12 - 15	15 - 18
KARAS, A., Dancing frogs	12 - 15	15 - 20

LIEBENWEIN, M. (Austria)

B.K.W.I., "Der Verrufene Weiher"	30 - 35	35 - 40

MÜLLER , R. (Austria)

"Der Apotheker"	18 - 22	22 - 25

    "Die Morgensuppe"

OHLER, C. (Hungary)

B.K.W.I., **Series 4678** (6)	20 - 25	25 - 28

PAYER, E. (Austria)

B.K.W.I. **Series 1748** (6)	15 - 20	20 - 25

  P.G.W.I. "Der Froschkönig"

V.S.M. The Frog King (Untitled)	15 - 18	18 - 22

R.R. (RUTTLEY, RALPH) (Germany)

M. Ettlinger Co., Dressed Frogs	15 - 20	20 - 25

SCHIFF, R. (Austria)
  W.R.B. & Co., Vienna
   Series 22-74 No Captions

The Frog King	15 - 18	18 - 22

SCHLITT, HEINRICH   Frogs & Elves Series
SCHONIAN, ALFRED

Elf and Frog Series	18 - 22	22 - 25

SCHUTZ, ERIC (Austria)
  B.K.W.I. Poster

41 "The Froschkönig"	25 - 30	30 - 35

SUSS, JOSEPH (Austria)
  GBWV

Series 55 "Der Froschkönig"	10 - 12	12 - 15

TWELVETREES, C. H. (U.S.)
  National Art Co.
    136 "Matinee Idol"   20 - 25   25 - 30
    137 "Paul and Virginia"
    138 "Come in the Water's Fine"
    139 "The Bride"
    140 "The Groom"
WESSEL, E. (Germany)
  B. Dondorf
    Series 28 "Sporting Frogs"   20 - 25   25 - 30
WIEGAND, MARTIN (Germany)
  Emil Kohn, München
    "The Frog King"   25 - 28   28 - 32
WINKLER, ROLF (Germany)
  NPG
    "Froschkönig"   12 - 15   15 - 18

PUBLISHERS

A.&M.B.
    Series 113 Chromolithos (6)   25 - 30   30 - 35
    Series 170 Chromolithos (6)
    Series 283 Chromolithos (6)   25 - 28   28 - 32
    Series 697 Chromolithos (6)
EAS, 1044 "The Frog Gardener"   20 - 25   25 - 28
HMB
    "Pfingsten" Series 3177 6)   18 - 22   22 - 25
    Series 2268 (6)
Humoristlish Postkarten
    Series 30   20 - 25   25 - 30
Kudka
    No. 36-450 Chromolitho
    "Volkssanger"   25 - 30   30 - 35
Kutzer & Berger, Berlin
    Series 202 Chromolithos (6)   22 - 25   25 - 30
Misch & Co.
    Series 403 Chromolithos (6)   20 - 25   25 -30
Misch & Stock
    No No. Chromolithos (6)
    Series 152 Chromolithos (6)
    "The Frog A-Wooing"   28 - 32   32 - 35
J. Mieser, Berlin
    Series 2000 Playing Musical Instr. (6) 18 - 22   22 - 25
M. Munk, Vienna
    Series 420 (6) Dance Series, Watercolors 22 - 25   25 - 28
OPF, Dressed Frogs, Very high Quality   40 - 50   50 - 60
Fritz Schardt, Nürnberg, Chromolithos   18 - 22   22 - 25

Arth. Thiele, TSN 1413
No Caption

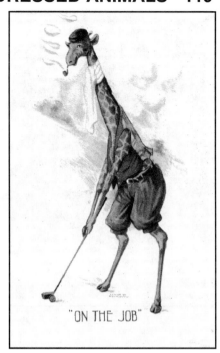

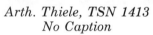

C. H. Twelvetrees, Ullman Mfg.
"Jungle Sports" 1895, "On the Job"

Raphael Tuck
    Oilette Series 294 (6) No Captions   22 - 25   25 - 30
    Series 1723 Chromolithos (6)
    Singing group - "Gruss Aus Weisbaden"   18 - 22   22 - 25
    Series 2598 (6)
Anonymous
    "Gruss Aus" Bregenz   22 - 25   25 - 28
    Frog Singers Series
    Concertsänger   30 - 35   35 - 45
    Mimesänger
    Natursänger
    Operettensänger
    Opernsänger
    Volkssänger
Advertising
Frog in the Throat Lozenge Co.
"Frog in the Throat" Series (12) (oversized)
1 "A Social Success"   45 - 50   50 - 60
2 "A Universal Favorite"
3 "Don't Be Without It"
4 "Favorite of all Times"
5 "Fore Everybody"   Golf   50 - 55   55 - 65
6 "For Singers"   45 - 50   50 - 55
7 "Innocent and Instantaneous"

Anonymous
"Fiscalitis"

8 "My Old Friend Dr. Frog"
9 "Needs No Introduction"
10 "Nothing Better"
11 "Pleasant to Take"
12 "Popular Everywhere"

"Frog in the Throat" Series (10) (oversized)	40 - 45	45 - 50
"Chicago Frogs" -- Bullfrog Brand	70 - 80	80 - 90
"Toledo Frogs" -- Bissel Carpet Sweepers (8)		
Baseball Frog	50 - 60	60 - 70
Golf Frog		
Others	40 - 45	45 - 50

GEESE

ELLAM, WILLIAM HENRY (G.B.)		
Raphael Tuck		
Series 9321 (1)	15 - 18	18 - 21

GIRAFFE

Miscellaneous	12 - 15	15 - 20
(Note: Prices reflect value of the artist.)		
ELLAM, WILLIAM HENRY (G.B.)		
Raphael Tuck		
Series II 9553 (1)	18 - 22	22 - 25

GOATS

Miscellaneous	12 - 15	15 - 18
(Note: Prices reflect value of artist.)		
See Witch Section		

GRASSHOPPERS

Miscellaneous	10 - 12	12 - 15
(Note: Prices reflect value of artist.)		

GROUNDHOGS

Henderson Litho Co.
    Ground Hog Day
    Comic Series 101

"Come out and make a shadow..."	125 - 150	150 - 200
"Don't get so chesty..."		
"May Miss Fortunes shadow..."		
"May the Shadow of your pruse..."	175 - 200	200 - 250

GUINNIPENS

HUDSON, G. M.
    R. Tuck
      Series 8648 (6)

"Guinnipen's Bedtime"	30 - 35	35 - 40
"Guinnipens Fishing"		
"Guinnipen's Saturday Night"		
"Guinnipens Shopping"		
"Guinnipen Truant"		
"Nurse Guinnipen"		

Anonymous
    "Fiscalitis"

HIPPOPOTAMUS

G.H.T. (Uns.)
    E. Nister
      Hippo Series 6 (6)

"But I don't mind another"	35 - 40	40 - 50
Others		

HORSES

Miscellaneous	12 - 15	15 - 18
See Arth. Thiele		

L. Meggendorfer, H.K.C.M. 265
Class Dunce?

L. Meggendorfer, H.K.C.M. 264
Cycling

L. Meggendorfer, H.K.C.M. 263
A Bit Windy?

Lionel Lindsay, Anonymous Publisher
"Possum Hurst" -- "Christmas Morning"

MONKEYS

MEGGENDORFER, L. (Germany)
   H.K.C.M.

Series 224	Monkeys Playing Cards (6)	18 - 22	22 - 25
Series 263	Monkey Mountain Hikers (6)		
Series 264	Monkey Sports (6)	22 - 25	25 - 30
Series 265	Intellectual Monkeys (6)	18 - 22	22 - 25

DOD, GIL (G.B.)
   S. Hildesheimer & Co.
   Series 5244 Sports (6)

"100 Yard Handicap"	25 - 30	30 - 35
"High Jump"		
"Obstacle Race"		
"Steeple Chase"		
Others		

THIELE, ARTH. (Germany)
   T.S.N.

Series 781 (6)	20 - 22	22 - 25
Series 844 (6)	22 - 25	25 - 30

WOOD, LAWSON (G.B)
   Valentine Pub. Co.
   Monkey Golf Cards

2457 "Tell Mother it Isn't..."	15 - 20	20 - 25
2759 "The Nineteenth Hole"		
Others	12 - 15	15 - 18

PUBLISHERS
   Ullman Mfg. Co.

"Monkey Doodle" Series 196	10 - 12	12 - 15

OPOSSUMS

CRITE (U.S.)
   HSV Litho Co., L. Gulick, 1909
   "Billy Possum Political Series" (12)

"Are You Dead - or Just Playing Possum?"	20 - 25	25 - 28
"Aw don't play possum"		
"The Boogie Man'll Get You..."		
"Dear Friends, My Home Address..."		
"Dear, Am unavoidably detained..."		
"Do it Now! Don't Play Possum; But..."		
"Give My Regards to Bill!"	25 - 30	30 - 35
"Good Eating Here!"	30 - 35	35 - 40
"I'm having a high old time..."	20 - 25	25 - 28
"It's a Great Game..." Golf	30 - 35	35 - 40
"Oo's 'ittle' possum is 'oo?"	20 - 25	25 - 28
"Very Busy; Both Hands Full..."		

DE WEES, ETHEL (U.S.)
   A.M.P. Co.

Frank J. Cohen & Son, Atlanta
Rare Political "Billy Possum"

EAS
"God Jul"

"Billy Possum " Series (6)		
"Arrived here just at right time"	25 - 30	30 - 35
"I'll make another drive..."		
"I'm going to make a record..."		
"It's a bad thing to put off..."		
"Just a few lines before game..."	28 - 32	32 - 35
"Yale's Favorite Son"		
LINDSAY, LIONEL (Australia)		
"Possum Hurst" -- "Christmas Morning"	15 - 20	20 - 25
PUBLISHERS		
Birn Brothers, (B.B., London)		
Series E243		
"We love BILLY POSSUM..."	28 - 32	32 - 35
Frank J. Cohen & Son, Atlanta, Ga.		
"Billy Possum" (B&W)	100 - 125	125 - 150
Lester Book & Stationery, Atlanta (1)		
Taft with Possum "Beat it Teddy Bear"	300 - 350	350 - 400
Fred C. Lounsbury (U.S.)		
Series 2515 (6) (Sepia)		
"The only Possum that escaped"	20 - 25	25 - 28
"Billy Possum and Jimmy P. on links"	28 - 32	32 - 35
"Good Bye Teddy"		
"Moving day in Possum Town"	20 - 25	25 - 28

Louis Wain
"A Breach of Promise Case"

"The Nation's Choice"	28 - 32	32 - 35
Series 2517 (6) (Blue tone)		
"Billy Possum to the Front"	20 - 25	25 - 30
"Columbia's Latest 'Possum and Taters"		
"Uncle Sam's New Toy"		
"The Nation's Choice"		
Others		
F. A. Owen Co. (B&W)		
"Billy Possum"		
"Hurrah for Bill and Old Eli"	40 - 50	50 - 60
Others		

OWLS

DUMONT	8 - 10	10 - 12
HERRFURTH, OSKAR (Germany)		
"Der Elf & Patents"	12 - 15	15 - 18
WAIN, LOUIS (G.B.)		
"A Breach of Promise Case"	100 - 125	125 - 150

PIGS

BARNES-AUSTIN, EDGAR (G.B.)		
Raphael Tuck		
"Piggie-Wiggie" Series (6)	12 - 15	15 - 18

Anonymous French
"April-April-April"

Unsigned, K.G.L. 9306
No Caption

Anonymous
"Viel Glück im neuen Jahre"

Carl Rogind, C.S.
"Gladeligt Nytaar"

Carl Rogind, C.S.
"Gladeligt Nytaar"

L. A. Govey, Frowde & Stoughten
"*A Tale of Woe*"

L. A. Govey, Frowde & Stoughten
"*In Disgrace*"

BERGER & OTTILLIE (Germany)
    Cycling Series   20 - 25   25 - 30
HORINA, H. (U.S.)
  Ullman Mfg. Co.
      Series 91 "Jimmy Pig" (10)
        1967 "This little pig went to market"   15 - 18   18 - 22
        1968 "This little pig went bathing"
        1969 "This little pig stayed home"
        1970 "This little pig went to school"
        1971 "This little pig went to a party"
        1972 "This little pig went to war"
        1973 "This little pig went fishing"
        1974 "This little pig worked in a garden"
        1975 "This little pig went sailing"
        1976 "This little pig was a drummer boy"
ROGIND, CARL (Denmark)
  C.S.
    Sports Series   20 - 25   25 - 30
THIELE, ARTH. (Germany)
  German American Novelty Art
      Series 789 Hog Head Studies (6)
      "I might be a Pig, but I'm no D. Hog"   20 - 25   25 - 30
      "Laugh and grow fat"
      "A Larder of So(w)ciety"
      "Ready for the Pi(g)nic"

MIND HOW YOU GO

Rene Cloke, J. Salmon Ltd. 6-38-53-92
"Mind How You Go"

"Sweet enough to eat"
"Such a Headache"

T.S.N.

Same series as 789 but without captions	25 - 28	28 - 32

PUBLISHERS

EAS "God Jul"	20 - 25	25 - 28
K.G.L. 9306 Well-dressed female pig		

ADVERTISING
Robeson Cutlery Co.

Red Pig Knives (10)	50 - 75	75 - 100

PIG CHIMNEY SWEEPS

	15 - 18	18 - 22
H.W.B. (Austria)	18 - 22	22 - 25
Others		

RATS/MICE

GOVEY, L. A. (G.B.)
Henry Frowde & Hodder & Stoughton
"The Little Mouse Family" (6)

"A Friend in Need"	22 - 25	25 - 28
"A Tale of Woe"		

"Fishing for the Moon"
"In Disgrace"
"Not on Squeaking Terms"
"The Old Woman Who Lived in a Shoe"

Others   12 - 15   15 - 18

SQUIRRELS

CLOKE, RENE (G.B.)
  J. Salmon Ltd.
    6-38-53-89 "A Pennyworth, Please"   8 - 10   10 - 12
    6-38-53-92 "Mind How You Go"
COWELL, CYRIL (G.B.)
  Bamforth Co.
    Series 1 "Squirrilquins" (6)   8 - 10   10 - 12
    Series 2 "Squirrilquins" (6)
DOVIE, E. H. (G.B.)
  Valentine's
    Series 704 (6)   8 - 10   10 - 12

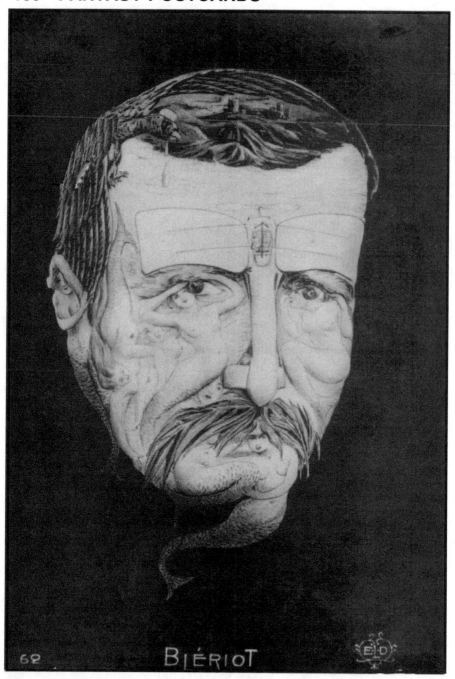

E.L.D. 62
Metamorphic, "BLÉRIOT," French Aviator

Chapter 5

Mermaids

The mermaid was a mythical creature that lived in the seas and streams. According to popular belief, they had bodies that were half human and half fish. Their beauty and mystique, as they sang and combed their long hair, was a great attraction for mortal men. A magical cap always lay beside them, and when the man they wanted appeared they would slip the cap on his head and take him away with them. A human being could live in the sea by wearing this cap. There were, on the other hand, mermen who also captured mortal maidens.

Through the years, mermaids and mermen have continued to be painted or dramatized in art and poetry. Certain sea animals; e.g., seals, look a little like humans from a distance. This similarity may explain the myths related to them.

The most beautiful mermaids on postcards are the works of Eric Schutz and Sofia Chiostri, "The Mermaid" series by Raphael Tuck, the Art Nouveau series by Gaston Noury, and the great early anonymous German chromolithographs. All are extremely scarce and are in great demand. Although there is no actual mermaid (with the upper body of a girl and lower body of a fish) shown, the Detroit Publishing Co. "Mermaid" series by S. L. Schmucker must be placed in this section. This series of six, with various fish and heads of beautiful ladies, are masterworks of art, and the best by any U.S. artist.

MERMAIDS

	VG	EX
ADOLF, T. (Germany)	$ 15 - 18	$ 18 - 22
ATTWELL, MABEL LUCIE (G.B.)		
Valentine & Sons		
951 (With Black Doll)	25 - 30	30 - 35
E.B. (Germany)		
M. L. Cartlens, Hamburg		
Series 5508 "Ein Guter Fang"	15 - 18	18 - 22
BENEZUR		
"Der Kampf"	16 - 18	18 - 22
BERNHARD, L. (Austria)		
Karl H. Detlefsen		
Series 3156 B&W "Ein Stelldichen"	12 - 15	15 - 18
BÖCKLIN, A. (Germany)		
F. Bruckmann AG		
"Play of Naiads"	12 - 15	15 - 18
"Im Spiel der Wellen"		
BOISSELIER (France)		
Salon des Paris		
1143 "Les Nerides"	8 - 10	10 - 12
BRUNNER		
Art Moderne Series 715 (6)	12 - 15	15 - 18

A. Bocklin, F. Bruckmann AG
"Im Spiel der Wellen"

Reg. Carter, M. Ettlinger 4453
Diver Series, "They fell in love..."

John Cecil Clay, Alfred Schweizer
1018, No Caption

BUXTON, DUDLEY (G.B.)
    Bamforth Co.
        "Ye Gods: It's the Missus!"   8 - 10   10 - 12
CARTER, REG. (G.B.)
    Max Ettlinger & Co.
        Series 4453 (Diver Series) (6)
        "A Diver walked along one day..."   18 - 22   22 - 25
        "They fell in love..."
        "Things cannot go on like this..."
        "They went for a walk..."
        "But true love not always runs smooth..."
        "Her father passed by that way..."
CHIOSTRI, SOFIA (Italy)
    Ballerini & Fratini
        Series 238 Cupid and Mermaid (4) Deco   50 - 60   60 - 75
        Series 317 (4) Deco
CLAY, JOHN CECIL (U.S.)
    Alfred Schweizer
        Gibson Karte 1018 No Caption, Sepia   15 - 18   18 - 22
COT, WILLIAM (France)
    AN, Paris Real Photo #224   15 - 18   18 - 22
DUBOSCLARD, PAUL (U.S.)
    M.A. Sheehan (Serigraphs)   10 - 12   12 - 15

*S. Chiostri, Ballerini & Fratini
Series 317, No Caption*

*S. Chiostri, Ballerini & Fratini
Series 238, No Caption*

*S. Chiostri, Ballerini & Fratini
Series 238, No Caption*

*S. Chiostri, Ballerini & Fratini
Series 317, No Caption*

*S. Chiostri, Ballerini & Fratini
Series 238, No Caption*

May Gibbs, Western Mail Postcards
"Pearling in the Norwest"

A. Guillaume, A. Noyer, Paris
"The Wreck"

FITZPATRICK (G.B.)		
Bamforth & Co.	8 - 10	10 - 12
FULLER, EDMUND G. (G.B.)		
"Midsummer Nights Dream" Series	15 - 18	18 - 22
GEO.		
Valentine's		
"Mr. Popple sees a Mermaid"	15 - 18	18 - 22
GIBBS, MAY (Australia)		
Western Mail Postcards (B&W)		
"Pearling in the Norwest"	80 - 90	90 - 100
GIRARDOT, GEORGES (France?)		
Societe des Artistes Francais		
"Siren at the mirror" (R.P.)	12 - 15	15 - 18
GOHLER, H.		
"Rishar" Russian		
566 "Du Nixlein Wunderhold..."	30 - 35	35 - 40
GRIMM (Austria)		
F. Morawetz, Salzburg		
No Caption	12 - 15	15 - 18
GUILLAUME, ALBERT A. (France)		
A.N., Paris		
"The Wreck"	20 - 25	25 - 30
Art Moderne		
Series 764		

Raphael Kirchner, Anonymous
"Flussnixe"

"Seetrift"	18 - 20	20 - 25
GUTMANN, BESSIE PEASE		
Rishar (Russian) Russian Caption		
"The Little Mermaid" - sitting on lily pad	75 - 100	100 - 125
H.F.	10 - 12	12 - 15
H.N.		
Rud. Stolle		
472 "Kuste bei Georgenwalde"	10 - 12	12 - 15
IRWIN	6 - 8	8 - 10
JACOBS, HELEN (G.B.)		
C. W. Faulkner		
Series 1764 (6)	18 - 22	22 - 25
KASPARIDES		
"Bath of Water Fairy"	15 - 18	18 - 22
KENNEDY, C. N. (G.B.)		
Leeds Gallery		
"The Mermaid"	5 - 6	6 - 8
KIRCHNER, RAPHAEL (Austria)		
Anonymous		
"Flussnixe"	150 - 200	200 - 250
KLEY, H. (Germany)		
EDM, Heidelberg		
366 "Rheingold, Rheingold!" (B&W)	10 - 12	12 - 15
LA PIERRE-RENOUARD (France)		
Lapina, Paris		
1312 "Idyll"	12 - 15	15 - 18

Anonymous Chromolithograph
Series 649, Wassernixen

Anonymous Chromolithograph
Series 649, Wassernixen

Private Mailing Card
German Chromolithograph

M. & L. G. National Series
Anonymous, No Caption

Grace O'Neill, Gibson Art Co. 96014
"For the Rainy Day"

LEEKE, F. (Germany)
   Munchener Kunst

3116 "De Taufe des Fawn"	15 - 18	18 - 22

LIEBENWEIN, M. (Austria)
   B.K.W.I.

1028 "Der Verrufene Weiher"	18 - 22	22 - 25

LUPIAC, A. P. (France)
   A.N., Paris

79 "Centaur and sea-maid"	25 - 28	28 - 32

M. I.
   W. de Haan (B&W)

Series 1020 (6)	10 - 12	12 - 15

MARAPAN
   Vetta

"The Neptune Myth" (1945)	10 - 12	12 - 15

MILLER, HILDA (G.B.)
   C. W. Faulkner

Series 1822 (6)	22 - 25	25 - 30

MUNSON, WALT (U.S.)
   Tichnor (Linen)

70327 "Fresh Guy"	6 - 8	8 - 10

   E. C. Kropp (Linen)

C43 "Believe it or not"	6 - 8	8 - 10

   Others

NOURY, GASTON (France)
   Anonymous

Series of (6) Chromolithographs	125 - 150	150 - 175

Walt Munson, Tichnor Bros. 70327
"Fresh Guy! I've Heard All About You Sailors"

Walt Munson, E. C. Kropp Company 29304
"Believe It Or Not, I Landed A 'Beauty' Today!"

*Anonymous Japanese Artist
and Publisher*

*ESD Series 8150
Embossed Art Nouveau*

O'NEILL, ROSE (U.S.)
  Gibson Art Co.

96014 "For the Rainy Day"	40 - 45	45 - 50

OUTHWAITE, IDA R. (Australia)
  A. & C. Black, London

Series 73 "Playing with Bubbles"	25 - 30	30 - 35

P.
  Povart

Series 39 "Darling! You're so different"	5 - 7	7 - 8

PAPPERITZ, G. (Germany)

Real Photos 151-12	10 - 12	12 - 15

M.E.P. (PRICE, MARGARET EVANS) (U.S.)
  C. M. Klump

Zodiac, Pisces (February & March)	12 - 15	12 - 18

PRINTZ, HANNS (Austria)
  T.S.N. Series 1370

"Das Rheingold"	40 - 45	45 - 50

RICHARDSON, AGNES (G.B.)
  Photochrom Co.

2018 "Now I've caught you"	20 - 25	25 - 30

ROTHAUG, ALEX (Germany)
  W. R. B. Co.

No. 4 "Nymphe"	20 - 22	22 - 25

E. Schutz, B.K.W.I. 885-5
Goethe's "Der Fischer"

E. Schutz, B.K.W.I. 979-5
Schubert's "Die Forelle"

E. Schutz, B.K.W.I. 391-3
"Heine's Der Mond ist..."

E. Schutz, B.K.W.I. 434-1
"Andersen's Marchen"

R. Tuck, Series 694
"The Rhine Gold"

E.S.D., Series 8160
"Das Rheingold"

RUAM (France)
    24   10 - 12   12 - 15
SADKO (Russia)
    "Canko" and Alexander III   20 - 25   25 - 30
SAGER, XAVIER (France)
    Big Letter Card
    "Un Baiser D'Ostende"   25 - 30   30 - 35
SCHMUCKER, S. L. (U.S.)
  Detroit Publishing Co., 1907
    "Mermaid" Series (6)
    Fish and girl facing front   200 - 225 225 - 250
    Trout and girl facing left
    Sea Horse and head of beautiful girl
    Fish and girl facing right
    Lobster and head of beautiful girl
    Goldfish and head of beautiful girl
SCHMUTZLER, L. (Germany)
  Hanfstaengl Co.   18 - 22   22 - 25
SCHREKHASSE, P. (Germany)
  S. Hildesheimer & Co., Series 5317 (6) 8 - 10   10 - 12
  Hans Kohler, Series 329 (6) 12 - 15   15 - 18
SCHUTZ, ERIC (Austria)
  B.K.W.I.
    Poster Cards

THE "MERMAID" SERIES
BY
S. L. SCHMUCKER (UNSIGNED)
PUBLISHED BY DETROIT PUBLISHING COMPANY © 1907

Fish and Girl
Facing Front

Trout and Girl
Facing Left

Fish and Girl
Facing Right

Goldfish and Girl
Facing Right

Lobster and Girl
Facing Right

Sea Horse and Girl
Facing Left

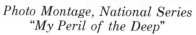

Photo Montage, National Series
"My Peril of the Deep"

Anonymous Silhouette
"Die Rhein Tochter"

203	"Flame of Love"	30 - 35	35 - 38
391-3	Heine - "Der Mond ist ..."		
434-4	Andersen's Märchen		
766-2	Schubert - "Das Wasser ..."	35 - 40	40 - 50
885-5	Goethe - "Der Fischer"		
979-5	Schubert - "Die Forelle"		

SHINN, COBB and YAD (U.S.)
  Anonymous (B&W)   10 - 12   12 - 15

SOLOMKO, SERGE (Russia)
  T.S.N.
    93 "The Tale"   15 - 18   18 - 25

STUDDY, GEORGE E. (G.B.)
  Bonzo Series by Valentine's
    Series 2982 "I'm a poor fish..."   12 - 15   15 - 18

TOLNAY (Hungary)
  Rotophot, Budapest (B&W)
    "Die Quelle"   15 - 18   18 - 22

WARNER, CHET (U.S.) Linens   8 - 10   10 - 12

WEISS, R. (Switzerland)
  A.W.R., Zurich
    "Auf Der Meersgrund" plus Mermen   12 - 15   15 - 18

WELLMAN, WALTER (U.S.)
    1026 "Beauty isn't all on the surface"   10 - 12   12 - 15

WHITE, FLORA (G.B.)
  W. E. Mack, Hampstead
    Poster - "The Little Mermaid"   18 - 20   20 - 25
  Photochrom Co.
    "Who are You?"   18 - 20   20 - 25
  J. Salmon Co. (6)   (Uns.)
    3820 "My Hat"   18 - 22   22 - 25
WILKIN, BOB   6 - 8   8 - 10
WINK
  L.P.
    2772 "Auf Stiller Flut"   12 - 15   15 - 18
WIWEL, KIRSTEN (Germany)   12 - 15   15 - 18
  Eneret
    Series 5047 (6) 1950's   8 - 10   10 - 12

PUBLISHERS
  American P. C. Co.
    Series 1319 (6)   10 - 12   12 - 15
  E.S.D. "Wagner" Series
    Series 8158
    Scenes from Opera "Seigfried"   25 - 30   30 - 35
    Series 8159
    Scenes from the Opera "Das Rheingold"
      No captions   30 - 35   35 - 40
    Series 8160 (Embossed) (6)
      Scenes from "Das Rheingold"
    Series 8164
    Scenes from Opera "Löhengrin"   25 - 30   30 - 35
  H & St. L.
    Series 7 (B&W)   6 - 8   8 - 10
  S. Hildeshimer & Co.
    Andersen's "The Little Mermaid"   20 - 25   25 - 30
  E. S. Lyon
    Series 122 (B&W)   8 - 10   10 - 12
  M. N. Co., 1910
    Unsigned and Unnumbered (10)
    "Come around and play with me"   20 - 22   22 - 25
    "Every Queen needs a King"
    "I want you and I want you right away"
    "If music be the food"
    "I'm leading an easy life"
    "I'll take another chance"
    "I'm going some nowadays"
    "I's Oo's little mermaid"
    "I'm hooked at last"
    "I'm looking for a partner"
    "Just meet me at the same old place"
    "Tag - You're it!"

This is eight in the series of ten cards copyrighted 1910 by M.N. The artist is unknown.

M.&L.G.		
National Series, Untitled		
Art Nouveau -- With Seashell	25 - 30	30 - 35
Mutoscope Co.		
Navy comics with mermaids	4 - 5	5 - 6
P.F.B. in Diamond		
S/R. Kammerer		
Series 6097	12 - 15	15 - 18
Percy, McG. Mann, Philadelphia (B&W)	10 - 12	12 - 15
S.W.S.B. Children Series	8 - 10	10 - 12
Salis, München (UndB) Chromolithos	40 - 50	50 - 60
Theo. Stroefer		
Series IV		
314 Mermaid in shell	15 - 18	18 - 22
H. H. Tammen		
"Here's to the girl..."	8 - 10	10 - 12
Curt Teich Linens		
3C-H549 Ad for Shedd Aquarium	12 - 15	15 - 20
Tichnor Bros. Linens		
"What I saw at..."	8 - 10	10 - 12
Others		
Raphael Tuck		
Series 3027 "Fun at the Seaside" (6)	12 - 15	15 - 18
Series 6822 "Mermaid" Series (6)	30 - 35	35 - 40
Series 694 "Wagner" Series (6)		
"The Rhine Gold"	30 - 35	35 - 40
Typo, Boston		
207 "There's something fishy"	6 - 8	8 - 10
Anonymous		
Art Nouveau Series 643 (6)	50 - 55	55 - 65
Copenhagen Statue (Early Real Photo)		
"La Petite Sirene"	4 - 5	5 - 6
1 er Avril (French April Fool) Montage	15 - 20	20 - 25
Japanese back, Unknown Artist	40 - 50	50 - 60
Montage (B&W)		
Series 12, #2, Girl's head/Mermaid body	15 - 18	18 - 22
Private Mailing Card (Chromolitho)		
Mermaid & Singing Frog	60 - 70	70 - 80
Real Photo Montage	18 - 22	22 - 25
Color Montage	15 - 18	18 - 22
Silhouette Poster "Die Rheintochter"	20 - 25	25 - 30
Series 643 German Chromolithos		
"Wassernixen" (6)	60 - 70	70 - 80
ADVERTISING		
Ackers Chocolates	30 - 35	35 - 40
Fish & Chips (A California Dish)		
Longshaw Card Co. Linen	12 - 15	15 - 18
Hartman Litho	10 - 12	12 - 15

D. P. Crane, H.G.Z. & Co.
Days of the Week -- "Sunday"

Chapter 6

Teddy Bears

The lovable and ever-popular Teddy Bears are very much in demand by postcard collectors who search for both artist-signed, unsigned, and real-photo types. Many great sets and series were published during the 1905-1914 era both in the U.S. and Europe, and are extremely popular with today's fantasy enthusiasts. A considerable number in this group are unsigned and, because of inadequate records by publishers, the artists have not been identified.

Collectors are indebted to Teddy Roosevelt and the U.S. press for the Teddy Bear. We are told that Mr. Roosevelt was invited to go bear hunting by some of his friends. After some period of time with no apparent success in finding bear meat, someone supposedly spotted one, but it turned out to be a little cub. Roosevelt refused to shoot the bear, and afterwards the press picked up on this unusual story of "Teddy's Bear." Thus, the Teddy Bear legend was born and the fad grew worldwide.

Books were written about the adventures of Teddy Bear, and toys and novelties of all types were generated. Publishers of postcards also took advantage of the terrific interest in the new fad. The resulting output of collectible cards was enormous, and many remain for the collectors of today. The "Roosevelt Bears," named after the President, are perhaps the most recognized of the sets or series and "The Cracker Jack Bears" are perhaps the most popular.

TEDDY BEARS

	VG	EX
BEM, E. (Russia)		
Russian "Rishar"	$ 20 - 25	$ 25 - 30
Russian Red Cross Soc. (St. Eugenia)		
Other Russian Publishers		
Lapina, Paris	15 - 20	20 - 25
BUSY BEARS (12)		
J. I. Austen Co.	15 - 18	18 - 22

    427 Monday (Washing)
    428 Tuesday (Ironing)
    429 Wednesday (Cleaning)
    430 Saturday (Mopping the Floor)
    431 Thursday (Mending)
    432 Saturday (Sewing)
    433 "Learning to Spell"
    434 "Playing Leap Frog"
    435 "Off to School"
    436 "Getting it in the Usual Place"
    437 "Something Doing"
    438 "Vacation"

	VG	EX
CAVALLY BEARS (Nursery Rhymes)		
CAVALLY, FRED (U.S.)		
Thayer Publishing Co., Denver	18 - 22	22 - 25

E. Bem, Rishar 1119
Russian Caption

J. I. Austen, "Busy Bears" Series 435, "Off to School"

J. I. Austen, "Busy Bears" Series 430, "Friday"

Fred Cavally, Thayer Publishing "What are little Ted Boys made..."

Fred Cavally, Thayer Publishing "Rain, rain, go away; ..."

"See-saw, Margery Daw"
"Rain, rain, go away"
"To make your candles last for aye"
"Cock crows in the morn"
"Little Red Snooks was fond ..."
"What are little Ted Boys made of?"
"As I went to Bonner"
"Nose, nose, jolly red nose"
"Dame Bear made a curtsy"
"Wash me, and comb me"
"Ding dong bell"
"Little Ted Grundy"
"Teddy be nimble"
"Multiplication is vexation"
"Tell Tale Tit!"
"Little Ted Horner"

ROSE CLARK BEARS (12)
    CLARK, ROSE (U.S.)

Rotograph Co., N.Y.	18 - 22	22 - 25
307 "Bear Town Cadet"		
308 "Is That You Henry?"		
309 "Henry"		
310 "The Bride"		
311 "The Groom"		
312 "A Bear Town Sport"		
313 "A Bear Town Dude"		
314 "I'm Going a-Milking"		
315 "I Won't be Home ..."		
316 "C-c-come on in"		
317 "Fifth Avenue"		
318 "Hymn No. 23"		

COLLINS BAKING CO. (4)	25 - 30	30 - 35

CRACKER JACK BEARS (16)
    B. E. MORELAND (U.S.)

Rueckheim & Eckstein		
1 At the Lincoln Zoo	30 - 40	40 - 50
2 In Balloon	30 - 35	35 - 40
3 Over Niagara Falls		
4 At Statue of Liberty		
5 At Coney Island		
6 In New York		
7 Shaking Teddy's Hand (Roosevelt)	35 - 45	45 - 50
8 At Jamestown Fair		
9 To the South	35 - 40	40 - 45
10 At Husking Bee		
11 At the Circus		
12 Playing Baseball	45 - 50	50 - 60
13 Cracker Jack Time	35 - 40	40 - 50

Rose Clark, Rotograph Co. 307
"A Bear Town Cadet."

Rose Clark, Rotograph Co. 314
"I'm going a-milking Sir,- ..."

Rose Clark, Rotograph Co. 317
"Fifth Avenue"

Rose Clark, Rotograph Co. 315
"I won't be home for dinner ..."

D. P. Crane, ZIM
"June"

A. R. Wheelan, Paul Elder & Company
"Doggerel Dodger," "This Bear's Witness..."

Cracker Jack Bears	*Cracker Jack Bears*	*Cracker Jack Bears*
Rueckheim & Eckstein	*Rueckheim & Eckstein*	*Rueckheim & Eckstein*
5, "To Coney Island..."	*8, "On Ship Board..."*	*9, "Away to South..."*

Cracker Jack Bears, Rueckheim & Eckstein
10, "Next to the Husking Bee..."

CRANE BEARS
    CRANE, D. P. (U.S.)
    H.G.Z. & Co. (ZIM)

"Days of the Week" (7)		15 - 18	18 - 22
"Months of the Year" (12)		18 - 22	22 - 25

Ellam Bears
B. Dondorf No. 347 (6)

Ellam Bears, B. Dondorf No. 370
"Prosit Neujahr!"

DOGGEREL DODGER BEARS
  WHEELAN, A. R. (U.S.)
  Paul Elder Co. (6)
    "This Bear's Witness..."   18 - 22   22 - 25
    Others
ELLAM BEARS
  B. Dondorf
    Series 347 (6) No Captions   15 - 18   18 - 22
    Series 370 (6)   18 - 22   22 - 25
  Raphael Tuck
    Series 9793 (6)   15 - 20   20 - 25
    Series 9794 (6)
    Others
HAHN BEARS
  SHEARER (U.S.)
  Albert Hahn Co. (A.H. in Trademark) (8)
    "En Route"   10 - 12   12 - 15
    "Happy"
    "In Court"
    "In War"
    "Just too Late"
    "Look Pleasant"
    "On Duty"
    "Painting the Town"

D. Hillson
"Thursday" -- *"Bear and Forbear"*

G. S., Langsdorff, Ser. 752
"Teddy Bear Orchestra No. 4."

Little Bears, Tuck Series 118
"Kept in at School"

Little Bears, Tuck Series 118
"Tobogganing in the Snow."

A. E. Kennedy, C. W. Faulkner & Co., Ltd.
"Somebody's been sitting on my chair!"

HEAL DAYS OF THE WEEK
  William S. Heal (U.S.)

"Sunday" Going to Church	10 - 12	12 - 15
"Monday" Washing Clothes		
"Tuesday" Ironing		
"Wednesday" Mending		
"Thursday" Baking		
"Friday" House Cleaning		
"Saturday" Shopping		
Same Series in Leather	12 - 15	15 - 18

HILDEBRANT (G.B.)
  Raphael Tuck
    Series 9792

Teddy Bears (6)	15 - 18	18 - 22

HILLSON DAYS OF THE WEEK
  D. Hillson

"Monday" Washday	10 - 12	12 - 15
"Tuesday" Ironing		
"Wednesday" Mending		
"Thursday" Baking		
"Friday" Cleaning		
"Saturday" Shopping		
"Sunday" Church		

KENNEDY, A. E.   15 - 18   18 - 22
  C. W. Faulkner & Co., Ltd.
    "Somebody's been sitting on my chair!"

Ottoman Lithographing Co.
"Good old summertime"

Ottoman Lithographing Co.
"Is marriage a failure?"

LANGSDORFF BEARS
  G. S.
    Teddy Bear Orchestra, No. 4   15 - 20   20 - 25
LITTLE BEARS
  Raphael Tuck
    Series 118 (12)   20 - 25   25 - 30
    "A Morning Dip"
    "A Very Funny Song"
    "Breaking the Record"
    "Kept in at School"
    "Missed Again"
    "Oh! What a Shock"
    "Once in the Eye"
    "The Cake Walk"
    "The Ice Bears Beautifully"
    "The Jolly Anglers"
    "Tobogganing in the Snow"
    "Your Good Health"
MARY'S BEARS
  C.L. (U.S.)
  Ullman Mfg. Co. (4)
    Series 119 (4)
    "Mary had a little bear..."   10 - 12   12 - 15
    "Everywhere that Mary went..."
    "It followed her to school one day..."
    "It made the children laugh..."
McLAUGHLIN BROS. BEARS
  McLaughlin Bros.   15 - 18   18 - 22
MOLLY & TEDDY BEARS
  GREINER, M. (U.S.)
  International Art Co.
    Series 791 (6)   15 - 18   18 - 22
OTTOMAN LITHOGRAPHING BEARS
  Ottoman Lithographing Co., N.Y.   15 - 18   18 - 22
    "Come Birdie Come"
    "Good Old Summertime"
    "Is Marriage a Failure?"

M.D.S., Ullman "Romantic Bears"
Series 88, "The Lullaby"

M.D.S., Ullman "Romantic Bears"
Series 88, "A Letter to My Love"

M.D.S., Ullman "Sporty Bears"
Series 83, "A Dip in the Surf."

M.D.S., Ullman "Sporty Bears"
Series 83, "Out for big Game"

"Many Happy Returns"
"Never Touched Me"
"Please Ask Pa"
"Right Up-To-Date"
"Well, Well, You never can Tell"
"Where am I at?"
"Will She Get the Lobster"

PILLARD (U.S.)
  S. Langsdorf & Co.
    Series 730

Teddy at Golf	22 - 25	25 - 28
Teddy at Soccer	18 - 22	22 - 25
Others		
S. S. PORTER BEARS (6)	8 - 10	10 - 12

ROMANTIC BEARS
  M.D.S. (U.S.)
  Ullman

Series 88 (4)	15 - 18	18 - 22

    1950 "Too Late"
    1951 "Who Cares?"
    1952 "The Lullaby"
    1953 "A Letter to My Love"

ROOSEVELT BEARS
  E. Stern Co. (First Series, 1906)

1 "At Home"	25 - 30	30 - 35

    2 "Go Aboard the Train"
    3 "In Sleeping Car"
    4 "On A Farm"
    5 "At a Country School"
    6 "At the County Fair"
    7 "Leaving the Balloon"
    8 "At the Tailors"
    9 "In the Department Store"
    10 "At Niagara Falls"
    11 "At Boston Public Library"
    12 "Take an Auto Ride"
    13 "At Harvard"
    14 "On Iceberg"
    15 "In New York City"
    16 "At the Circus"

  Second Series

17 "Out West"	60 - 70	70 - 80

    18 "Put out a fire"
    19 "At the Wax Museum"
    20 "At West Point"
    21 "As Cadets"
    22 "In New York"
    23 "In Philadelphia"
    24 "At the Theatre"

Roosevelt Bears, Stern 32
"The ... at Washington"

Roosevelt Bears, Stern 2
"The ... go Aboard the Train"

Roosevelt Bears, Stern 26
"The ... at Independence Hall"

Roosevelt Bears, Stern 30
"The ... on a Pullman"

25 "Swimming"		
26 "At Independence Hall"		
27 "Celebrate the Fourth"		
28 "At the Zoo"		
29 "Go Fishing"		
30 "Bears on a Pullman"		
31 "Hunters"	80 - 90	90 - 100
32 "At Washington" (With Roosevelt)	35 - 40	40 - 50
Third Series (no captions)		
17 "Lighting Firecracker" (horizontal)	250 - 275	275 - 300
18 "Celebrating the Fourth" (horizontal)		
19 "Waving Flags"		
20 "Ringing Liberty Bell"		
No No. Series		
Roosevelt Bears in Canada	250 - 275	275 - 300
Roosevelt Bears in England		
Roosevelt Bears in Ireland		
Roosevelt Bears in Scotland		
Roosevelt Bears in Switzerland		
The Roosevelt Bears "Return from abroad"		

ROWNTREE, HARRY (G.B.)

    C. W. Faulkner & Co.

Series 236 (6)		
"I am collecting"	22 - 25	25 - 28
"I am coming up to see you"		
"I'm feeling a bit off color"		
"The Weather is Perfect"		
Others		
Williston Press		
Same images as Series 236	15 - 18	18 - 22

SPORTY BEARS

    M.D.S. (U.S.)

    Ullman Mfg. Co.

Series 83 (7)		
1923 "Love All"	12 - 15	15 - 18
1924 "Here's for a Home Run"	15 - 18	18 - 22
1925 "Out for Big Game"	10 - 12	12 - 15
1926 "King of the Alley"		
1927 "A Dip in the Surf"		
1928 "An Unexpected Bite"		

ST. JOHN BEARS

    ST. JOHN

    Western News Co.

161 "Spring"	12 - 15	15 - 18
162 "Summer"		
163 "Autumn"		
164 "Winter"		

    V.O.H.P. Co.

      Series X40

Harry Rowntree, C. W. Faulkner
Ser. 236, "I am collecting"

Harry Rowntree, C. W. Faulkner
Ser 236, "I'm feeling a bit off..."

Days of the Week (7)	10 - 12	12 - 15
TEDDY BEAR BREAD (Advertising) (4)		
DENSLOW, W. W. (U.S.)		
1-3	30 - 45	45 - 60
4	50 - 60	60 - 75
TEMPEST, MARGARET		
Medici Society		
Series 61 (6)	10 - 12	12 - 15
TOWER TEDDY BEARS		
Tower M. & N. Co. (30)	10 - 12	12 - 15
"Beary Well, Thank You"		
"But We Are Civilized"		
"Did You Ever Wear..."		
"Don't Say a Word"		
"Here's to the Stars and Stripes ..."		
"Hurrah for - Eagle"		
"Hurrah for the..."		
"I'm Waiting For You"		
"Our Birth, You Know"		
"We Wear Pajamas"		
"You Don't Say"		
Others		
T. P. & CO. TEDDY BEARS		
T. P. & Co.	10 - 12	12 - 15

Tower M. & N. Company
"Here's to the Stars and Stripes ..."

"Out for Airing"
"I Wonder if He Saw Me?"
"Isn't He a Darling"
"How Strong He Is"
"Oh! My! - He's Coming!"
"Off for the Honeymoon"
"Little Girl with Teddy"
"Dolly Gets an Inspiration"
"Lost, Strayed, or Stolen"

TWELVETREES BEARS
  TWELVETREES, CHARLES

National Art Co. (6)	10 - 12	12 - 15

    206 "Little Bear Behind"
    207 "Stung"
    208 "The Bear on Dark Stairway"
    209 "How can you Bear this Weather?"
    210 "A Bear Impression"
    211 "The Seashore Bear"

National Art Co.		
271 "It's Up to You"	10 - 12	12 - 15

WALL, BERNHARDT

Ullman "Busy Bears" Series 79	10 - 15	15 - 18

    1905 Sunday
    1906 Monday
    1907 Tuesday
    1908 Wednesday

THURSDAY
This Little Bear Bakes Pies.

SUNDAY
This Little Bear Goes to Church.

*B. Wall, Ullman "Busy Bears"
Series 79, "Thursday..."*   *B. Wall, Ullman "Busy Bears"
Series 79, "Sunday ..."*

1909 Thursday		
1910 Friday		
1911 Saturday		
Ullman "Little Bears" Series 92	12 - 15	15 - 18
WELLS BEARS (7)	8 - 10	10 - 12
ANONYMOUS		
(Vine Through Post Card) Flat Printed		
241 "I am in a whirl"	6 - 8	8 - 10
242 "I'm certainly enjoying myself"		
243 "I never expected to meet you"		
244 "Oh my but you are sweet"		
245 "I have not had much luck so far"		
246 "I am not going anywhere..."		
247 "The joys of a bachelor's life"		
248 "It was a touching scene"		
249 "Stuck again"		
250 "I have been hunting for you"		
REAL PHOTO TEDDY BEARS		
With Children (Large Bears)	25 - 35	35 - 45
With Children (Small Bears)	20 - 25	25 - 30
With Ladies (Large Bears)	18 - 22	22 - 28
With Ladies (Small Bears	12 - 15	15 - 20
Bears Alone (Large)	15 - 20	20 - 25
Bears Alone (Small)	12 - 14	14 - 16

Real Photo
Ca 1910

Real Photo
Ca 1915

Meissner & Buch, No. 3329
"Glücklische Fahrt in's neue Jahr!"

Bears and Movie Stars	10 - 12	12 - 15
OTHER ARTIST-SIGNED TEDDY BEARS		
With Children (Large Bears)	10 - 15	15 - 20
With Children (Small Bears)	8 - 12	12 - 15
With Ladies (Large Bears)	10 - 12	12 - 18
With Ladies (Small Bears)	8 - 12	12 - 15

Additional listings of Bears can be found under "Bears" in the Dressed Animals Section.

Fröhliche Weihnachten!

Very Rare Signed Ellen Clapsaddle Child Santa with Switches
Anonymous -- "Fröhliche Weihnachten!"

Chapter 7

Santas

Santa Claus is a mythical old man who visits at Christmas and brings toys and goodies to children who have been good throughout the year. In the U.S. he is plump and jolly, wears red suits, and has a twinkle in his eyes. European Santas, depending on the country, are called Father Christmas, St. Nicholas, Nicolo, and other names.

The German Father Christmas, or "Weihnachtensmanner," is very thin, wears fur-trimmed robes of various colors, and sometimes has an angel to assist and guide him on his long and countless journeys. Occasionally, he is also seen carrying the Christ Child. However, most cards portray him as having a very stern countenance and he may be seen carrying switches to punish mean children. Both St. Nicholas and Nicolo have the impish devil Krampus as their helper.

Probably the most avidly collected cards of all time are Santas. In greatest demand are the early chromolithographs and embossed issues of German origin with robes of colors other than red. Robes of yellow, orange, black, and gray are those in the "most wanted" category. The outstanding works of A. Mailick, the Hold-to-Light issues, and the PFB and Winsch are also in great demand.

It is impossible to identify all the many hundreds of great Santas because many are not signed and do not have a publisher byline. Some have only a series number of "Printed in Germany" as the only means of identification. This is especially true of those not published for American distribution.

SANTAS

	VG	EX
ARTIST-SIGNED		
BOWLEY, A. L. (G.B.)		
Raphael Tuck		
Series **512** (6)	$ 25 - 30	$ 30 - 35
Series **C1758**		
Series **C2099**		
Series **8437, 8449**		
BRUNDAGE, FRANCES (U.S.)		
Raphael Tuck		
Series **4** (12)	20 - 25	25 - 28
Series **525,** Santa Scroll Series (6)	12 - 15	15 - 20
Series **1822** (6)	30 - 35	35 - 40
Sam Gabriel		
Series **200**	15 - 20	20 - 25
Series **230**		
BAUMGARTEN, FRITZ Or F.B. (Germany)		
Comical Santas, various color robes	20 - 25	25 - 30

CA, Czech Publisher
Child Santa (Yellow Suit)

Green Robed German Santa
Anonymous Publisher

BEATY		
AH	8 - 10	10 - 12
CA		
Czech Publisher		
Child Santa in yellow Suit	20 - 25	25 - 30
CLAPSADDLE, ELLEN (U.S.)		
International Art		
Signed	18 - 22	22 - 25
Unsigned	15 - 18	18 - 22
Anonymous German		
Child Santa with Switches (Very Rare)	50 - 60	60 - 75
Other German unsigned issues	20 - 25	25 - 35
CHIOSTRI, S. (Italy)		
Ballerini & Fratini		
Series 220 Black Robes (4)	50 - 60	60 - 75
Others	30 - 35	35 - 45
EBNER, PAULI (Austria)		
B. Dondorf	25 - 30	30 - 35
M. Munk		
FP Anonymous Publisher, Foreign Caption	175 - 200	200 - 225
GASSAWAY, KATHARINE (U.S.)		
Raphael Tuck		
Series 501	20 - 25	25 - 40
HBG (H. B. GRIGGS) (U.S.)		
L & E		
Series 2224		
Black Robe	30 - 35	35 - 40
Green Robe	25 - 30	30 - 35
Others	20 - 22	22 - 25
Series 2264		
Black Robe	30 - 35	35 - 40
Others	20 - 22	22 - 25
Series 2275		
Brown Robe	25 - 30	30 - 35
Others	18 - 20	20 - 22
HARPER, R. FORD (U.S.)		
Lady Santas (4)	30 - 35	35 - 45
HOGER, A. With Christ Child	30 - 35	35 - 40
HZONEY, CH. (Czech.)		
Anonymous French Publisher	110 - 120	120 - 130
KIRCHNER, RAPHAEL (Austria)	325 - 350	350 - 400
KÖHLER, MELA (WW) (Austria)	500 - 525	525 - 575
MBH		
Raphael Tuck		
Series 549 "Santa Claus" (6)	12 - 15	15 - 18
MEG		
Raphael Tuck		
Series 535 "Santa Claus" (6)	10 - 12	12 - 15

Uns. Clapsaddle, Meissner & Buch
"Fröhliche Weihnachten"

Anonymous White-Robed Santa
"God Jul"

MAILICK, A. (Germany)
   Hold-To-Light

Red Robe	150 - 250	250 - 350
Robes of other Colors	250 - 300	300 - 400
Early Chromo-Lithographs	25 - 50	50 - 100
W.W.		
Series 6308	65 - 75	75 - 85
Series 6670 (with Christ Child)	75 - 80	80 - 90
Red Robe	40 - 50	50 - 65
Robes of other Colors	65 - 75	75 - 100
St. Nicholas & Krampus Series	35 - 40	40 - 45
MAUFF, S. A. (Stengel Art Nouveau)	200 - 225	225 - 275
NYSTROM, JENNY (Sweden)		
Red Robes	15 - 18	18 - 22
Robes of other Colors	20 - 25	25 - 30
SANDFORD, H. D. (G.B.)		
Raphael Tuck Series 8247, 8248 (6)	18 - 22	22 - 25
SCHONIAN (Germany)		
T.S.N. Series 1090 Various Color Robes	30 - 35	35 - 40
SCHUBERT, H. (Austria) Various Color Robes	25 - 30	30 - 35
SHEPHEARD, E. (G.B.)		
Raphael Tuck Series 8415, 8421 (6)	15 - 18	18 - 22
WAIN, LOUIS (G.B.)		
M. Ettlinger, Cat Santa Series 5376	300 - 350	350 - 400

A. Mailick, W.W. 6308
No Caption

A. Mailick, W.W. 6670
"Fröhliche Weihnachten"

Wrench, Cat Santa Series	175 - 200	200 - 225
Note: See Cat Santa on Back Cover.		
GERMAN SANTAS		
LARGE FULL FIGURES		
(Old World, thin figures)		
Black Robe	50 - 60	60 - 75
Gray or White Robe	40 - 45	45 - 50
Blue, Tan or Purple Robe	35 - 40	40 - 45
Yellow or Orange Robe	45 - 50	50 - 60
Brown or Wine Robe	30 - 35	35 - 40
Striped, Two-color or Art Deco	45 - 50	50 - 60
Red Robe	15 - 20	20 - 25
HEADS, Upper Body or Small Image		
(Valued at 50%, or less, than Full Figures.)		
HOLD-TO-LIGHT (See H-T-L Section)		
FULL FIGURES		
Red Robes	200 - 300	300 - 400
Robes colored other than red	300 - 400	400 - 500
HEADS, Upper Body or Small Image		
Red Robes	200 - 300	300 - 350
Robes colored other than red	300 - 350	350 - 400
TRANSPARENCIES	75 - 100	100 - 125
MECHANICALS		
Honeycomb Folders	60 - 70	70 - 80

Anonymous (Possibly Langsdorf)
"Merry Christmas"

St. Nicholas, PFB 8935
No Caption

Anonymous, Chromolithograph
Foreign Caption

Anonymous, Series 2508-1
Foreign Caption

Anonymous Uncle Sam Santa
Knocking on Door, Flat Printed

Louis Wain, M. Ettlinger 5376
"With best Wishes for a Happy..."

Pop-outs	35 - 40	40 - 45
Pull-tabs	250 - 300	300 - 400
Stand-ups	50 - 75	75 - 100
Wheel-type	200 - 250	250 - 300
SILK APPLIQUE		
FULL FIGURES		
Langsdorf	40 - 50	50 - 60
AMB	35 - 40	40 - 45
Others	25 - 30	30 - 35
SMALL FIGURES	15 - 20	20 - 25
UNCLE SAM SANTAS		
(1) **Flat-Printed** (4)	600 - 650	650 - 750
(2) **Embossed** (4)	700 - 800	800 - 900
(3) **Squeakers** (4)	1600 - 1650	1650 - 1700
(4) **Hold-to-Light** (4)		
a. Santa Knocking on Door	2750 - 3200	3200 - 3800
b. Santa Trimming the Tree		
c. Santa Standing on Step		
d. Santa at Window (bag of toys)	3200 - 3500	3500 - 4200
PUBLISHERS		
AA (Anglo American)		
Series 705, 708, 709 (6)	12 - 15	15 - 20
AMB Silks	35 - 40	40 - 50

Valentine and Sons, "Christmas in Coonland:
We've come to meet yo', Massa Santy Claws!"

FP, Yellow-Robed Black Santa
Anon. Publisher, French Caption

Ch. Hzoney, White-Robed Santa
Anon. Publisher, French Caption

AMP		
Modes of transportation	12 - 15	15 - 20
Others	8 - 10	10 - 12
ASB		
Series 87 Various color robes	30 - 35	35 - 40
Barton & Spooner	6 - 8	8 - 10
B.W., Germany		
Series 291, 296, 305, 324	15 - 18	18 - 20
Series 297	20 - 25	25 - 30
MAB		
Series 15850 Chromolithos	25 - 30	30 - 40
R. L. Conwell	10 - 12	12 - 15
Julius Bien		
Series 500	10 - 12	12 - 15
Series 5000		
EAS	20 - 25	25 - 30
Child Santas	30 - 35	35 - 40
Gibson Art	6 - 8	8 - 10
Sepia	5 - 6	6 - 7
International Art		
Signed Clapsaddle	18 - 22	22 - 25

ASB, 87 (Purple Robe)
"God Jul"

L&B, 16284 (Blue-Gray Robe)
Russian Caption

P. Sander Silk Santa
"A Merry Christmas"

SWSB 8650 (Blue Coat)
Foreign Caption

Unsigned Clapsaddle	15 - 18	18 - 22
L&B		
Series 16284 **(Blue-Gray Robe)**	25 - 30	30 - 35
Langsdorf		
Series 1320	20 - 22	22 - 28
Silks	40 - 50	50 - 60
M.M.B.	15 - 18	18 - 22
J. Marks		
Series 538 (6)	5 - 8	8 - 10
Meissner & Buch		
S/F.B.	20 - 25	25 - 28
E. Nash		
Series 3 Heads, Smoking pipe	12 - 15	15 - 18
Series 18		
Nister, E.		
Series 2046 (6)	30 - 35	35 - 40
Series 2409 (6) Small images	20 - 25	25 - 28
PFB (Paul Finkenrath, Berlin) (Emb.)		
Series 5431, 6227, 7933 (6)	40 - 45	45 - 50
Series 7312, 6481 (6)	25 - 30	30 - 35
Series 7930, 5434 (6)	20 - 22	22 - 25
Series 6434, 9593 (6)	35 - 40	40 - 45
Series 6439, 8935 St. Nicholas (6)	35 - 40	40 - 45
Other St. Nicholas Series	30 - 35	35 - 40

Other Santas	25 - 30	30 - 35
Robbins Bros.		
Series 1163 Old Style (6) (Emb.)	25 - 30	30 - 35
Rotograph Co.		
H3025 Black Robe	60 - 70	70 - 80
SB		
Series 433, 7519 (6) Old Style	30 - 35	35 - 40
S&M		
Series 36	20 - 25	25 - 28
Series 149 "Big Sack" Series		
Samson Bros.		
Series 31, 705 (6)	12 - 15	15 - 20
Series 3102	25 - 28	28 - 32
Sander, P.		
Lady Santas (4) -- Signed Harper	35 - 40	40 - 50
Black Santa - No No. Full Figure	100 - 125	125 - 150
No No. Full Figure	15 - 18	18 - 22
Stecher Litho. Co.		
Series 55, 1555 (6)	8 - 10	10 - 12
Series 61, 203, 314, 504 (6)	10 - 12	12 - 15
Series 68 Uns. James E. Pitts	12 - 15	15 - 20
Series 213 (6)	12 - 15	15 - 18
Series 227 (6)	15 - 18	18 - 22
Series 732, 737 (6)	10 - 12	12 - 15
Reprints of 1930's, 40's	3 - 4	4 - 5
S.W.S.B.		
Red Robes	20 - 22	22 - 25
Other Color Robes	30 - 35	35 - 40
P. Sander		
Large Images	20 - 25	25 - 28
Silk Santas	30 - 40	40 - 50
Santway		
Large Images, various color robes	30 - 35	35 - 40
Series 1251 Small Images	10 - 12	12 - 15
Souvenir P.C. Co.		
Series 426	8 - 10	10 - 12
Raphael Tuck* **		
Series 1, 102, 8000, 8619	30 - 35	35 - 40
Series 5, "Kris Kringle"	10 - 12	12 - 15
Series 55, 1029, 1744	25 - 30	30 - 35
Series 1766 Chromolithos	40 - 45	45 - 50
Series 136, 501	10 - 12	12 - 15
Series 512, 535, 806	12 - 15	15 - 18
Series 505, "The Christmas Series"	25 - 30	30 - 35
White Robes	40 - 50	50 - 60
Series 576B	25 - 30	30 - 35
Colors other than red	30 - 35	35 - 40
Series 1803	15 - 18	18 - 22
Series 8263	25 - 30	30 - 35

Series 8267, 8320	15 - 18	18 - 22
Series 8620 Various Color Robes	25 - 30	30 - 35
No No. Series "Christmas Postcards"	10 - 12	12 - 15

* Most series contain cards of children.
* Most series contain 6 cards.

Ullman Co.

National Santa Claus Series 2000	25 - 30	30 - 35

Valentine and Sons

"Christmas in Coonland: We've come to..."	300 - 400	400 - 500

WB

Series 307	10 - 12	12 - 15

George C. Whitney

Full Santas	15 - 18	18 - 22
Small Figure Santas	8 - 10	10 - 12

John Winsch*

Copyright 1912 - Vertical (4)

Red Robe, yellow/gold background	25 - 30	30 - 35

"A Joyful Christmas"
Red Robe, green background
"A Merry Christmas"
Santa on gold background
"I Wish You a Merry Christmas"
Orange Robe, blue background
"May Your Christmas be Bright..."

Copyright 1912 - Vertical (4)

Children watch Santa in plane	18 - 22	22 - 26

"A Merry Christmas"
Child watching Santa's shadow
"A Joyful Christmas"
Child watching Santa around chimney
"Best Christmas Wishes" (Horizontal)
Children see Santa coming from chimney
"A Joyful Christmas"

Copyright 1912 - Vertical (2)

Red Robed Santa with Teddy Bear and	35 - 40	40 - 45

   Golliwogg at chimney
"Best Christmas Wishes"
Santa in red jacket, blue-striped
   pants flying bi-plane
"A Happy Christmastide"

Copyright 1913 - Horizontal (4)

Red Robe, Teddy Bear, Smokes pipe	40 - 50	50 - 60

"Best Christmas Wishes"
Red Robe, teddy bear, jack-in-box"
"Christmas Greetings"
Red Robe, with arm-load of dolls
"Christmas Wishes"
Red/Pink Robe carrying bag of fruit

John Winsch, © 1912
"I Wish You a Merry Christmas"

Uns. S. L. Schmucker, Winsch
Back, "A Merry Christmas"

Winsch, © 1914 (Booklet Add-on)
64891, "A Merry Christmas"

John Winsch, © 1913
"A Christmas Greeting"

Real Photo	Tinted Real Photo, French
U.S.	DEDE 1315

"Merry Christmas"
Copyright 1913 - Horizontal (4)
    Santa in airplane tosses toys to
        children on balcony   25 - 30   30 - 35
    "A Joyful Christmas"
    Santa in airplane tosses toys to
        children on ground
    "A Joyous Christmas"
    Children watch Santa in balloon basket
    "A Merry Christmas"
    Children on balcony watch Santa with
        toys in airplane
    "A Christmas Greeting"
Copyright 1913 - Vertical (2)
    Red Robe, driving car, big clock   25 - 30   30 - 35
    "Christmas Greetings"
    Santa driving motor bus
    "A Christmas Greeting"
    Red Robe, two Children...one on back
    "Best Christmas Wishes"
    Red Robe, kissing one of two children
    "A Joyful Christmas"
    Red Robe, one of two children whispers
    "A Merry Christmas"

Copyright 1914 - Vertical
  Add-on, Santa and children on bell
No Copyright Date
  Red & Gold Borders, Horizontal
  Children greet Red Robe Santa at door   50 - 55   55 - 60
  "Christmas Wishes" -- No. 4164
  Children greeting Santa from bed
  "A Merry Christmas"
* With Silk or Ribbon Inserts add $3-5.
REAL PHOTOS
  French & European
    Black & White   10 - 15   15 - 18
    Tinted   15 - 18   18 - 20
    St. Nicholas   10 - 15   15 - 18
  U.S. Real Photos   15 - 20   20 - 30
    Tinted   20 - 25   25 - 35

OTHER SANTAS
  Child Santas   20 - 25   25 - 35
  Lady Santas   25 - 30   30 - 40
  Santa W/Christ Child - Add $10.
  Santa W/Switches - Add $5 - $10.
  Santa W/Angels - Add $5.00.
  Santa Switching Child - Add $5 - $10.
  Santa W/Odd Transportation - Add $5 - $10.
    Airplanes - Add $5.
    Autos - Add $5.00
    Balloons - Add $5.00
    Boats, Canoes - Add $5.00
    Donkey - Add $6.00
    Motorcycle - Add $7.
    Parachute - Add $8.
  Santas in Zeppelins   25 - 100   100 - 200
  Santa W/Golliwogg - Add $10.
  Santa W/Teddy Bear - Add $5.
  Santa W/Krampus - Add $10 - $15.
  Santa Smoking Pipe - Add $5.
  Santa and Mrs. Claus - Add $10.

SAINT NICHOLAS, NICOLO
  PFB Series 6439   25 - 30   30 - 35
  Real Photo Types   10 - 12   12 - 15
  Wearing Red/white Robe
    Full Figure   20 - 25   25 - 30
    Small Figure, Head or Upper Body   10 - 12   12 - 15
  Wearing Robes other than Red/White
    Full Figure   25 - 30   30 - 35
    Small Figure, Head or Upper Body   15 - 18   18 - 22

Krampus at His Very Best ... Ready for the Ladies!

B.K.W.I., Series 2840/II
"Diebesten Grüsse vom Krampus"

Chapter 8

Krampus!

Krampus was the impish devil with one cloven hoof who helped Saint Nicholas distribute toys, gifts, fruits, and nuts during the Christmas season, especially in Austria, Czechoslovakia and some other European countries. While traveling with Nicholas he played with and was good to the children who had been good. However, he always carried chains and a big bundle of switches, and made use of a large basket on his back to help in the storage and later punishment of children and adults who had been bad.

Those who knew they had been bad in any way quickly scurried away to escape his wrath. Krampus, however, chased and always caught them and put them in his basket. This terrified them, thinking they were going to be switched or thrown in the flames. The crying children or adults were later released after promising Krampus they would be on their best behavior during the coming year.

He was also painted as a being very suave and debonair around the pretty ladies, and many cards imply that they welcomed his passionate advances toward them. However, it was not so with the older and ugly ladies. He usually made fun of them or threw them into burning flames.

The cards of Krampus, being part of the fantasy world, are highly desirable and very collectible. The early 1900's images, especially those signed by artists and without the red backgrounds, command very high prices. Cards by artists of the highly regarded Wiener Werkstaette and any containing Art Nouveau renderings are especially in demand, as are those with both Krampus and St. Nicholas together on the same card.

On early Krampus cards, collectors will find that many artists signed only their initials or did not sign them at all. Most of the red background cards are unsigned, making them less desirable. Krampus cards are a continuing tradition, much like our Santas, and are still being produced for each Christmas season. Therefore, collectors must be wary and be sure of the era of the cards they plan to buy. All listings below are pre-1930.

KRAMPUS

	VG	EX
B.F.	$ 12 - 15	$ 15 - 18
BOURGET (Austria)		
Lady Krampus	30 - 35	35 - 40
BRAUN, W. H. (Austria)		
W.R.B. & Co.		
Series 22 (32)		
Krampus and lady on see-saw	25 - 30	30 - 35
Others, with beautiful ladies		
C.B.		
Georg Wagrandl, Wien		
Russian Krampus teased by soldiers	30 - 35	35 - 40
CR		
A.R., Wien		
Girl Krampus	25 - 30	30 - 35
DIVEKY, JOSEF VON (Hungary)		
Wiener Werkstaette, 238	300 - 500	500 - 750
(Note: See back cover.)		
DOCKER, E. (Austria)		
Series 45 (6) K. & Nicholas Series		
K. lights Nicholas' pipe	25 - 28	28 - 32
K. and cat		
Others		
Series 83 Krampus & Nicholas Series (6)	20 - 25	25 - 30
Others		
DYLER		
B.K.W.I.		
Krampus Series	18 - 22	22 - 25
EBERLE, JOSEF (Austria)		
Deutschen Schulverein, 122	30 - 32	32 - 35
EBNER, PAULI (Austria)		
M. Munk		
Krampus and children (6)	25 - 30	30 - 35
ENDRODI (Austria)		
Lady Krampus plays Diabolo	22 - 25	25 - 30
F.G.		
K. jumps through fire	22 - 25	25 - 28

W. H. Braun, W.R.B. & Co.
Series 22-31

Josef von Diveky
Wiener Werkstaette, 238

Th. Fasche, M. Munk 1086
"Gruss vom Krampus!"

Anonymous
Polish Krampus

FASCHE, TH. (Germany)
  M. Munk, Wien

No. 1086	20 - 22	22 - 25

G.L.
    Little Krampus looks down in basket

GEL, H. (Austria)

Mean Krampus with kids (6)	25 - 28	28 - 32
Silhouettes (6)	18 - 22	22 - 25
GELLARO	20 - 25	25 - 30

H.
    Series 234 (6)

Krampus with old ladies	25 - 28	28 - 32
Krampus wrestles old lady	25 - 28	28 - 32

H.B.

Krampus & Nicholas Series (6)	22 - 25	25 - 30
Others		

H.G.
  H.H.i.W., Wien
    Series 695

K. hands lady to Devil in furnace	25 - 30	30 - 35
Others		

    Series 568
    Krampus with crying boy

H.W.	15 - 18	18 - 22

FEIERTAG, KARL (Austria)

Child Krampus Series (6)	15 - 18	18 - 22

HARTMANN, A. (Austria)
  C.H.W. VIII
    Series 2460 (6)

K. whips lovers; kids in basket	25 - 30	30 - 35

    K. and kids above hot flames
    K. and Nicholas. K. whips kids
    Kids play ring-around K. with adults in
      basket
    Series 2489 (6)

K. with kids in baskets, flames behind	30 - 35	35 - 40

    Series 2490 (6)
    K. with lovers in basket, switching kids
    Series 2491 (6)
    K. watches lovers. Kids in chains, basket.

HATZ, H. (Austria)

Dachshund dressed as Krampus	25 - 28	28 - 32
Others		

HETZEL (Austria)
  B.K.W.I.
    Series 2013 (6)

K. dressed as a dandy	25 - 28	28 - 32
Others		

Josef Eberle
Deutschen Schulvereines 122

CH, A. R., Wien
Girl Krampus

H.G., H.H.i.W. Series 695
"Gruss vom Krampus"

A. Hartmann, C.H.W. VIII/2
Ser. 2489, "Gruss vom Krampus!"

A. Hartmann, C.H.W. VIII/2
Ser. 2491, "Gruss vom Krampus!"

A. Hartmann, C.H.W. VIII/II
2490, "Gruss vom Krampus!"

Anonymous
TEHO, Wien

KUDERNY, F. (Austria)
  B.K.W.I.
    Series 2601 (6)
      Toy Krampus   15 - 18   18 - 22
      Others
KUTZER, ERNST (Austria)
  B.K.W.I.
    Series 3236 (6)
      Krampus listens to angel   20 - 22   22 - 25
      Girl on skis with small Krampus
      Krampus behind angel
      Others
  Deutschen Schulverein
      Kids fight Krampus and Nicholas   25 - 30   30 - 35
      Small Krampus and Nicholas on skis
      Others
M.S.H.   Little Krampuses   15 - 18   18 - 22
MAILICK, A. (Germany)
      Krampus and St. Nicholas   25 - 30   30 - 35
      Others
MORAUS
      St. Nicholas and Krampus   22 - 25   25 - 28
O.W.
      Women as Krampus   25 - 28   28 - 32
OHLER, C. (Hungary)
  B.K.W.I.
    Series 2565 (6)
      Krampus sits on wall front   25 - 28   28 - 32
      Krampus sits on wall, reading
      Krampus standing, hands clasped
PAL
      Krampus and Nicholas in autos   15 - 18   18 - 22
PAYER, E. (Germany)
      Krampus and St. Nicholas   25 - 30   30 - 35
SASULSKI, K. (Poland)
  Pocztowski 269
      Krampus and St. Nicholas   30 - 35   35 - 40
SCHEINER (Czech)
      K. leads rich man away from his money   25 - 28   28 - 32
SCHÖNPFLUG, FRITZ (Austria)
  B.K.W.I.
    Series 2586
      Thinly built Krampus - red striped shorts   30 - 35   35 - 38
      Krampus carries officer on shoulders
      Krampus sits on stool, brushes hair
      Krampus tweaks chin of ugly old lady
      Krampus sits on mean bulldog's house
      Krampus hates tennis players

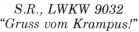

S.R., LWKW 9032
"Gruss vom Krampus!"

Unsigned Schönpflug
B.K.W.I. Series 2586-3

Series 22 (6)		
Red-faced K. with woman in basket	30 - 35	35 - 38
Girl in red - as Krampus		
Krampus whips boy as children cry		
Krampus upsets tennis players	35 - 40	40 - 45
Krampus with boy in basket, others running	30 - 35	35 - 38
Krampus holds man over flames		
SINGER, SUZI (Austria)		
Wiener Werkstaette, 319, 320	750 - 900	900 - 1000
B.K.W.I. (6)	50 - 60	60 - 125
T.W.		
Girl Krampus and Nicholas	30 - 35	35 - 38
WIENER WERKSTAETTE Artists *	300 - 1000	500 - 1500
* See Miscellaneous Section for fantasy		
input on other Wiener Werkstaette Artists		
PUBLISHERS		
B.K.W.I.		
Series 2017 (6)	20 - 25	25 - 28
Series 2840/II (6) (Emb., Red B.G.)		
Suavely dressed Krampus Series	25 - 30	30 - 35
Series 3041 (6)	15 - 20	20 - 25

C.H.W.
    Series 2461 (6)
      Man-woman in basket, K. switches kids   28 - 32   32 - 35
      Others
    Series 2502 (6) Red B.G.
      Kids give Krampus hard time   12 - 15   15 - 18
EAS
    Krampus pulls girl's pony tail (Emb.)   30 - 35   35 - 38
    Others
Erika
    Series 2 (6) K. and St. Nicholas   15 - 18   18 - 22
H.H.i.W.
    Series 1608 (6)   25 - 30   30 - 35
    Series 1626 (6)
    Series 1628 (6)
      Krampus chases beautiful lady   30 - 35   35 - 38
LP
    Series 3977
      Krampus with mean kids   35 - 38   38 - 42
LWKW, 9000 Red B.G. Series (10)   12 - 15   15 - 18
M. Munk, Wien
    Series 1043 (6)
    K. & Nicholas Series   25 - 30   30 - 35
O.K.W.
    Series 1633
      Krampus & Nicholas (6)   28 - 32   32 - 35
O.P.F.   60 - 75   75 - 125
SB
    Series 3180
      Crying girl in basket   25 - 30   30 - 35
    Others
"TEHO"
    Giant Krampus head eating kids   28 - 32   32 - 35
Anonymous Polish Krampus   28 - 32   32 - 35

MISCELLANEOUS

Pre-1920 Artist drawn   15 - 18   18 - 22
1920-1940 Artist drawn   12 - 15   15 - 18
Pre-1920 Black on red background   15 - 20   20 - 25
1940+ Black Krampus on red background   5 - 8   8 - 10
1940+ Artist drawn
With add-on switches   10 - 12   12 - 20
Felt of Krampus in tuxedo   40 - 50   50 - 55
Full-face large, embossed   40 - 50   50 - 100
Silk sack & switches on embossed card   25 - 30   30 - 35

Hanns Printz, T.S.N. S-1370, "Löhengrin"

Hanns Printz, T.S.N. S-1370, "Die Meistersinger von Nürnberg"

This series commemorates the 100th anniversary of Wagner's birth. It contains six of his most important operas, the others being "Das Rheingold," "Die Walküre," "Parsival" and "Tannhäuser."

Chapter 9

Wagner

The German composer Richard Wagner, who many think was the greatest composer who ever lived, died in 1883 but left a legacy that would live forever. It is believed that he alone fundamentally changed European musical, literary, and theatrical life. To Germans and other Europeans he was a great man, and at the turn of the century his operas continued to be a passion for all who loved music and the theatre.

Wagner's first opera was *Rienzi* and then came *The Flying Dutchman.* Later came his famous *Tannhäuser* and *Löhengrin*, which were operas concerning the romantic views of medieval life. His greatest creation, however, was *The Ring of the Nibelungs*, which actually was four operas in one ... *The Rhine Gold, The Valkyrie, Siegfried,* and *The Twilight of the Gods*.

The love story of *Tristan and Isolde* was one of his most popular, and *The Mastersingers of Nürnberg* was his only mature comedy. Wagner's final work was *Parsifal*, an opera with a religious theme about early Spain and the Holy Grail.

German artists, because of their great love for the works of Wagner, painted many beautiful fantasy sets and series about the heroes and heroines of his operas. The great poster-type cards by Hanns Printz, Heinz Pinggera, and Eric Schutz are certainly of epic proportions. Also, the works by Raphael Tuck and ESD of paintings by Franz Stassen are among the best in a very wide field.

WAGNER OPERA FIGURES

	VG	EX
AIGNER		
Series 259 (6)		
4490 "Tannhäuser"	$ 8 - 10	$ 10 - 12
AUBERT, PAUL (Germany)		
27 "Tannhäuser" B&W	8 - 10	10 - 12
BAUFCHILD		
"Löhengrin" (6)	10 - 12	12 - 15
BERGMULLER, C.W.		
Nude "Walküre"	12 - 15	15 - 20
BRAUNE, ERWIN (Germany)		
Nude "Walküre"	12 - 15	15 - 20
DOUBEK, F. (Germany)		
Ackerman		
"Elisabeth" - Tannhäuser	15 - 18	18 - 22
"Elsa" - Löhengrin		
"Sieglinde" - Walküre		
ERLAND, P. V. (Germany)		
"Brünhilde"	8 - 10	10 - 12
"Löhengrin"		
"Rienzi - Rienzis Gebet"		

Erwin Braune, Amag Kunst
"Walküre"

H. Fründt, M. Kimmelstiel & Co.
"Walküre"

F. Kuderny, Dutschnationalen
Dereines, "Die Nibelungen"
"Kriemfild"

F. Kuderny, Dutschnationalen
Dereines, "Die Nibelungen"
"Siegfried"

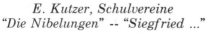

E. Kutzer, Schulvereine
"Die Nibelungen" -- "Siegfried ..."

Heinrich Lefler, M.M. 1261
"Ortrud." -- "Löhengrin"

FAHRENKROG, LUDVIG (Germany)
    298 "Parsifal"   8 - 10   10 - 12
    520 "Parsifal"
FRÜNDT, H. (Germany)
  M. Kimmelstiel & Co.
    "Walküre"   20 - 22   22 - 25
GLOTZ, A. D. (Germany)
    "Parsival" Series   10 - 12   12 - 15
    Series 22   8 - 10   10 - 12
GOETZ (Germany)   8 - 10   10 - 12
HENDRICHS (Germany)
  Poster
    "Siegfried's Tod"   15 - 18   18 - 22
HOFFMAN, H. (Germany)
    "Siegfried" (6)   12 - 15   15 - 18
JANOWITSCH
  B.K.W.I.
    3219 "Parsifal"   8 - 10   10 - 12
KLIMESOVA, M.
    "Walküre"   8 - 10   10 - 12
KUDERNY, F. (Austria)
  Poster Cards
  Deutsch. Dereines fur Osterreich
    "Die Nibelungen"

Ferd Leeke, M. Munk 861
"*Siegfried*"

Ferd Leeke, M. Munk 982
"*Götterdämmerung*"

"Kriemfild"	15 - 18	18 - 22
"Siegfried"	15 - 18	18 - 22
Others		

KUTZER, E. (Austria)
Poster Cards
B.K.W.I.
    Series 438 (6)

1 "Tannhäuser"	20 - 25	25 - 28
2 "Der Filegende Hollanders"		
3 "Meistersinger"		
4 "Parsifal"		
5 Wagner's "Rienzi"		
6 "Löhengrin"		

Vereines Sudmark

245 "Die Meistersinger von Nürnberg"	22 - 25	25 - 28
246 "Die Meistersinger von Nürnberg"		
247 "Die Meistersinger von Nürnberg"		
248 "Löhengrin"		
249 "Tristan und Isolde"		
252 "Tannhäuser"		
253 "Die Walküre"	22 - 25	25 - 28
254 "Das Rheingold"		
255 "Siegfried"		
256 "Siegfried"		

Schulverein fur Osterreich
"Die Nibelungen"
Poster Cards (8)
    "Siegfried und der Trache" (Dragon)   18 - 22   22 - 26
L.R.
    1096 "Parsifal"   10 - 12   12 - 15
    1097 "Siegfried"
    Others
LEEKE, FERDINAND (Germany)
  M. Munk, Vienna
    Series 861 (12)
    "Die Feen"   8 - 10   10 - 12
    "Die Meistersinger"
    "Die Walküre" (The Valkyrie)
    "Götterdämmerung" (Twilight of the Gods)   10 - 12   12 - 14
    "Löhengrin"   8 - 10   10 - 12
    "Parsifal"   10 - 12   12 - 14
    "Rienzi"   8 - 10   10 - 12
    "Rheingold"   10 - 12   12 - 14
    "Siegfried"   8 - 10   10 - 12
    "Tannhaüser"
    "Tristan und Isolde"   10 - 12   12 - 14
    "Tristan und Isolde"
    Series 982 (12)
    Same images as **Series 861**   8 - 10   10 - 12
    984 and E984 (12) Reprint of **Series 861**   6 - 8   8 - 10
  Hanfstaengl's Kunstlerkarte
    Series 72 (6)
    "Die Walküre"   10 - 12   12 - 15
    "Götterdämmerung"
    "Löhengrin"
    "Siegfried"
    "Tannhäuser"
    "Tristan und Isolde"
  H.K. Series 12   Same as series 72   10 12   12 - 15
  Poster Cards
  P/L. Pernitzch
    "Richard Wagner's Heldengestalten" (24)
    1 "Rienzi"   15 - 18   18 - 22
    2 "Der Fliegende Holländer"
    3 "Der Fliegende Holländer"
    4 "Tannhäuser"
    5 "Tannhäuser"
    6 "Tannhäuser"
    7 "Löhengrin"
    8 "Löhengrin"
    9 "Tristan und Isolde"
    10 "Tristan und Isolde"

Heinrich Lefler, M.M. 1281
"Eva." -- "Die Meistersinger"

H. Pinggera, Bund der Deutschen
242, "Siegfried"

H. Pinggera, Bund der Deutschen
249, "Parsifal"

H. Pinggera, Bund der Deutschen
250, "Tannhäuser im ..."

11 "Tristan und Isolde"
14 "Die Walküre"
15 "Die Walküre"
16 "Die Walküre"
17 "Siegfried
18 "Siegfried"
21 "Götterdämmerung"
22 "Götterdämmerung"
23 "Götterdämmerung"
24 "Götterdämmerung"

Hanfstaengels
Series 72
"Die Walkyrie" III   8 - 10   10 - 12
Others

LEFLER, PROF. HEINRICH (Austria)
M. Munk, Vienna
Wagner's Frauengsetalten
Series 1281 (6)
"Brünhilde" - Götterdämmerung   15 - 18   18 - 22
"Elisabeth" - Tannhäuser
"Elsa" - Löhengrin
"Eva" - Die Meistersinger
"Fricka" - Die Walküre
"Isolde" - Tristan and Isolde
"Ortrud" - Löhengrin

LUDVIG   **Series 718** (6)   8 - 10   10 - 12
NOWAK, OTTO (Germany)
B.K.W.I.
Series 1412
"Parsival"   8 - 10   10 - 12
Series 2352
"Wotan"   8 - 10   10 - 12
PEETE   "Siegfried" and the Dragon   12 - 15   15 - 18
PETER, O. (Germany)
Series 399
"Brünhilde"   12 - 15   15 - 18
PILGER
"Tannhaüser" (With Music)   10 - 12   12 - 15
PINGGERA, HEINZ (Austria)
Poster Cards
Bund der Deutchen in Niederösterrich
Series 242-252   18 - 22   22 - 25
242 "Siegfried"
248 "Herr Olof"
250 "Tannhaüser im Sorfelberg"
750 "Götterdämmerung"
751 "Die Walküre"
752 "Tannhaüser"

Eric Schutz, B.K.W.I. 205-1
"Parsifal"

Eric Schutz, B.K.W.I. 438-5
"Rienzi"

Eric Schutz, B.K.W.I. 438-6
"Löhengrin"

Eric Schutz, B.K.W.I. 206-6
"Parsifal"

PRINTZ, HANNS (Austria)
  T.S.N. (Theo. Stroefer, Nürnberg)
    Series 1370 (6) Chromolithographs

"Das Rheingold" Mermaid	30 - 35	35 - 40
"Die Meistersinger von Nürnberg"	25 - 30	30 - 35
"Die Walküre"		
"Löhengrin"		
"Parsival"		
"Tannhäuser"		

ROWLAND, FR. (Germany)
  Series 258

"Parsifal"	18 - 22	22 - 25

SCHLIMARSKI
  Series 420 (6)

1 "Parsifal"	10 - 12	12 - 15
Others		

SCHUTZ, ERIC (Austria)
  B.K.W.I.
    Series 205 Musical Posters (6)

1 "Wagner - Parsifal"	22 - 25	25 - 28
4 "Wagner - Parsifal"		
6 "Wagner - Parsifal"		
Others		

    Series 438 Posters

1 "Tannhäuser"	22 - 25	25 - 28
2 "Der Fliegende Holländers"		
3 "Meistersinger"		
4 "Tristan & Isolde"		
5 "Rienzi"		
6 "Löhengrin"		

SINZ, MAX

4 "Wotan"	8 - 10	10 - 12
Others		

SPIELZ, A.
  Series 247 (6)

4423 "Parsival"	10 - 12	12 - 14

STASSEN, FRANZ (Germany)
  H & A Bruning
    Richard Wagner Series (6)

5990 11 "Elsa"	20 - 25	25 - 28
6991 III "Venusburg"		
6992 IV		
6993 V "Brünhild"		
6994 XIV "Senta"		

  Raphael Tuck
    "Wagner" Series

Series 690 "Siegfried"	22 - 25	25 - 28
Series 691 "Löhengrin"		

Franz Stassen, E.S.D. 8158
"Siegfried"

Franz Stassen, E.S.D. 8164
"Löhengrin"

Franz Stassen, R. Tuck 1219
"Parsifal"

F. Stassen, H. & A. Brüning 6993
Series V, "Brunhild"

Hanns Printz, T.S.N. S-1370
"Das Rheingold"

Series 692 "Götterdämmerung"
Series 693 "Tristan and Isolde"
Series 694 "The Rheingold"
Series 695 "The Flying Dutchman"
Modern Meister XX Series 1219 (6)
"Götterdämmerung"   15 - 20   20 - 25
"Löhengrin"
"Parsifal"
"Rheingold"
"Siegfried"
"Tristan und Isolde"
E.S.D. (Unsigned Stassen)*
German and American Art Nouveau Series
   8157 "Die Walküre" (6)   18 - 22   22 - 25
   8158 "Siegfried" (6)
      Add $5 for Dragon Images.
   8159 "Das Rheingold" (6)
      Add $10 for Mermaid Images
   8160 "Götterdämmerung" (6)
   8161 "Die Meistersinger" (6)
   8162 "Tristan und Isolde" (6)
   8163 "Der Fliegende Holländer" (6)
   8164 "Löhengrin" (6)   12 - 15   15 - 18
* Same caption number on both U.S. and German
TOEPPER, HANS (Germany)
  F. A. Ackerman, Munchen (Continental size)

Series 625 "Ring des Nibelungen" (12)	12 - 15	15 - 18
TOUSSAINT		
"Isolde"	8 - 10	10 - 12
WEISLEIN		
"Barbarossa" Poster	10 - 12	12 - 15

PUBLISHERS

B. & W.		
271 "Siegfried's Death"	12 - 15	15 - 18
B.K.W.I.		
Series 206 (6)	12 - 15	15 - 18
Series 438 (6)		
Wilhelm Boehme		
"Altgermanische Gotter" (6)		
625-630	12 - 15	15 - 18
F.M.K. 3153 "Löhengrin" (6)		
FRG		
Series 247 "Parsifal" (6)	12 - 15	15 - 18
Series 258 "Löhengrin" (6)		
C.W. Faulkner 1401 "Die Feen"	12 - 15	15 - 18
M. Munk, Vienna		
Wagner's Series 28		
Ricordi & Co.		
"Siegfried & the Dragon"	8 - 10	10 - 12
Ladies in Wagner's Operas	12 - 15	15 - 18
Series 861 (12)	10 - 12	12 - 15
Series 982 (6)		
Series 984 (6)		
T.S.N. (Theo. Stroefer)		
Series 141 "Löhengrin" (6)	15 - 18	18 - 22
Raphael Tuck *		
"Wagner" Series		
690 "Siegfried" (6)	18 - 22	22 - 25
Add $5 for Dragon Images		
691 "Löhengrin" (6)		
692 "Götterdämmerung" (6)		
693 "Tristan and Isolde" (6)		
694 "The Rheingold" (6)		
Add $10 for Mermaid Images		
695 "The Flying Dutchman" (6)		
* Same as E.S.D. Series Above		
Series XX, 1219 "Modern Meister" (6)		
Same Captions as "Wagner" Series (6)	18 - 22	22 - 25
Stengel & Co.		
29132 "Die Walküre"	8 - 10	10 - 12
Others		
Ottmar Zieher		
Wagner's Operas (6)	25 - 28	28 - 32

O. Michaelis, P.F.B. 4416
"Centaur und Nymphe"

Chapter 10

Nude Fantasy

Nude Fantasy cards are very special to collectors of color nudes. Rather than simple paintings of the female form, various themes were used to make them more appealing and exciting. The greater part of this material originated in Europe, especially in the German countries where nudity was looked on as a thing of beauty and was not so far removed from the public eye. The strict mores of the American public kept nudes of all types away from the collecting fraternity.

Perhaps one of the most prevailing themes of Nude Fantasy was that relating to Biblical or Christian characters; e.g., a beautiful nude image of Eve with a deadly snake, Salome with the severed head of John the Baptist, or a lion stalking a horrified nude in the arena. Others focused on the nude and wild animals, of which many are available.

The wonderful series of beautiful nudes and giant snakes by Suzanne Meunier and the fantasy nudes of Eric Schutz are a definite highlight of this group. Additionally, the fine works of S. Schneider and Hugo Hoppener (who used the pen name of Fidus) have made their real photos the most collectible in the field. The Fidus real photo series of young girls entitled "Temple Dance" is clearly exceptional, as are many of his exquisite graphic illustrations. All of these help to make Fantasy Nudes one of the most enticing themes for postcard collectors today.

NUDE FANTASY

	VG	EX
BENDER, S.		
H.R. "La Femme" Series		
Reclining nude with animals (12)		
1217 With parrot	$ 20 - 25	$ 25 - 28
1220 With monkey and spider		
1222 With cat		
Others		
(Snakes)	12 - 15	15 - 18
BEROUD, L.		
Salon 1901		
Series 201-20 "Fantasie" Tiger and nude	15 - 18	18 - 22
BÖCKLIN, A. (Germany)		
Bruckmann A. G.		
6 "Die Nereide"	12 - 15	15 - 18
16 "Im Meere" (Nude and Merman)	10 - 12	12 - 15
21 "Triton & Nereide" (Merman)	10 - 12	12 - 15
"Spiel der Wellen" Nudes and Horse-man	12 - 15	15 - 20
BRAUNE, E. (Austria)		
Amag Kunst		
63 "Walküre" (Horse)	12 - 15	15 - 18

S. Bender, H.R. Series 1220
"La Femme"

A. Cabanel, Salon J.P.P. 2206
"Nymph and Faun."

Courselles Dumont, Salon de 1912
47, "In the Arena"

E. Fischer-Coerlin, M.K.B. 2475
"Salome"

C. A. Geiger, Marke J.S.C. 6112
"Salome"

CABANEL, A.
  Salon J.P.P.
    2206 "Nymph & Faun" (Man-Goat)   15 - 18   18 - 22
COURSELLES DUMONT, H. (France)
  Lapina
    564 "In der Arena" (Lion)   12 - 15   15 - 20
  Salon de 1912
    47 "In the Arena" (Lion)
DE BOUCHE, A. (Germany)
  Moderner Kunst, Berlin
    2516 "Salambo"   15 - 18   18 - 22
DUSSEK, E.A. (Austria)
  J.K.
    69 "Froschkönigs Braut" (Frog)   22 - 25   25 - 28

FIDUS

Among the most beautiful fantasy real photo nudes on postcards are the graphic works of Hugo Hoppener (who used the pen name of Fidus). He did great drawings of nude and sometimes erotic young ladies and young boys, plus many others, for his books, posters and magazines. In most of his works he used very precise graphic border illustrations which greatly enhanced their beauty.

To advertise and sell these works he published real photo advertising postcards, describing each of them, and distributed the cards widely. It is not known just how successful he was in selling his works with the cards, but the cards themselves have become extremely popular with collectors. The series entitled "Tempeltanz der Seele" (Temple Dance of the Soul) of young maidens standing on fantasy petals, leaves, stems and the Universe, is probably the most sought after by today's collector. However, Fidus did many others in the fantasy vein that are also in great demand.

FIDUS or Hugo Hoppener (Germany)
  N.B.C. (Real Photos)
    2 "DrachenKampfer" Nudes and Dragon   25 - 28   28 - 32
    101 "Tempeltanz Der Seele I"   30 - 35   35 - 40
    102 "Tempeltanz Der Seele II"
    103 "Tempeltanz Der Seele III"
    104 "Tempeltanz Der Seele IV"
    105 "Tempeltanz Der Seele V"
    106 "Tempeltanz Der Seele VI"
    134 "Erwartung" Nude in white birch grove 20 - 25   25 - 30
    393 Nude and statue of Wagner   20 - 25   25 - 30
    515 "Neapmierinatais Lucifers" Satan   20 - 25   25 - 30
    Many other Fantasy types

Fidus, St. Georgs-Bundes 102
"Tempeltanz der Seele II"

Fidus, St. Georgs-Bundes 103
"Tempeltanz der Seele III"

Fidus, St. Georgs-Bundes 105
"Tempeltanz der Seele V"

Fidus, St. Georgs-Bundes 135
"Sterntänzerin"

Others - non Fantasy	12 - 15	15 - 18

FISCHER-COERLINE (Germany)
  M.K.B.

2475 "Salome" (Severed Head)	18 - 22	22 - 25

GEBHARDT, CARL (Germany)
  E.M.

132 "Loreley"	20 - 25	25 - 28

GEIGER, C. A. (Hungary)
  Marke J.S.C.

6109 "Liebeskampf" (Man-Sea Beast)	18 - 22	22 - 25
6112 "Salome" (Severed Head)		

GIOVANNI, A. (Italy)
  ARS Minima

119 "Salome" (Severed Head)	12 - 15	15 - 20

GLOTZ, A. D. (Germany)
  B.K.W.I.

1009 "Lebensluge" (Ghost of Dead)	12 - 15	15 - 18
HIRSCH	10 - 12	12 - 14

HOESSLIN, GEORGE
  NPG

491 "Die Schaumgebstene" (Nude in Oyster Shell)	10 - 15	15 - 18

C. A. Geiger, Marke J.S.C. 6109
"Liebes Kampf"

Ch. Lenoir, Lapina 5122
"Victory!!!"

Prof.
Rich. Müller
Dresden
Perlen

Prof. Rich. Müller, N.P.G.A. 251
"Perlen"

HORST (Germany)
   P.F.B. in Diamond

4323 Semi Nude and Horse Drink	12 - 15	15 - 18

ICHNOWSKI, M. (Poland)
   Series 90

16 Nude and Lion	18 - 22	22 - 25

KANDLER, V. (Germany)

Nude and Snake	15 - 18	18 - 22

KELLER, F. (Germany)
   Russian Publisher

076 "Finale" (Death Head)	15 - 18	18 - 22

KOMINEL   15 - 18   18 - 22
KORPAL
LAMM
LANGENMANTEL

Nude on Bull	12 - 15	15 - 20

LEEKE, F. (G.B.)
   Munchener Kunst

3113 "Nidre und Wasserman"		
(Water Creature)	12 - 15	15 - 20
3114 "Gefangene Nymphe" (Dwarfs)		
3117 "Triton Belaufde Nereide" (Merman)	15 - 18	18 - 22

LENOIR, CH. (France)
   Lapina

5122 "Victory!!" (Octopus)	22 - 25	25 - 28

LEOPAROVA
KV
1183 "Salome" (Severed Head)	12 - 15	15 - 20

LINS, ADOLF
EAS
607 "Faun and Nymphe"	12 - 15	15 - 18

MANDL, J.
Minerva
177 "Printemps" (Wings)	10 - 12	12 - 15

MASTAGLIO
Galerie Munchener Meister
380 "Duell" (Nudes Fencing)	12 - 15	15 - 20

MASTROIANNI, C. (Italy)
198 "Fievre d'Amore" (Waterfall)	10 - 12	12 - 15

MEUNIER, SUZANNE (France)
MARQUE L. E.
Series 64 (6) Nudes & big snakes	35 - 40	40 - 45

MICHAELIS, O.
P.F.B.
Series 4416 "Centaur und Nymphe"	20 - 25	25 - 30

MUHLBERG, GEORG (Germany)
Nude Riding a Seahorse.	12 - 15	15 - 18

MÜLLER, PROF. RICH (Austria)
251 Nude riding goldfish "Perlen"	20 - 22	22 - 25
252 Nude with red Ibis		

MÜLLER-BAUMGARTEN (Germany)
FEM
161 "Faun & Nymphe" (Man-Goat)	10 - 12	12 - 15

MUTTICH, C. V. (Czech)
V.K.K.V.
2077 "Sulejka" (Peacock)	12 - 15	15 - 20

OKON, T.
Stella, Bochina
1233 Nude and black cat	12 - 15	15 - 20

PENOT, Albert (France)
Lapina
1340 "Red Butterfly" (Red-Winged Nude)	12 - 15	15 - 20

PIOTROWSKI, A. (Poland)
Minerva
505 Woman/Children/Serpent	15 - 20	20 - 25
1028 "Salome" (Severed Head)	18 - 22	22 - 25

Manke JSC
6082 "Charmeuse de Serpents" (Snake)	15 - 18	18 - 22

PODKOWSKI (Poland)
Nude on wild Horse	18 - 22	22 - 25

REINACKER, PROF. G. (Germany)
PFB
6082 "Schlangen-Bandigerin" (Snake)	15 - 18	18 - 22

Marke J.S.C.
  6082 Same as above
ROTHAUG, ALEX (Germany)
  LP

2815 "Pan and Psyche" (Man-Beast)	15 - 18	18 - 22

  W.R.B. & Company

No. 4 "Nymphe"	12 - 15	15 - 18

ROWLAND, FR. (G.B.)
  SVD

379 "Sirenen" (Snakes)	18 - 22	22 - 25

ROYER, L. (France)
  Salon de Paris

374 "La Sirene" (Death Head)	12 - 15	15 - 18

RÜDISÜHLI, EDUARD
  K.E.B.

"The Demon of Love"	12 - 15	15 - 18

SAMSON, E. (France)
  A.N., Paris

243 "Diane" (Wolf Dogs)	15 - 18	18 - 22

SCALBERT, J.
  S.P.A.

48 "Leda & the Swan"	10 - 12	12 - 15

Fr. Rowland, SVD 379
"Sirenen"

Eric Schutz, B.K.W.I. 885-2
"Der Gott und Die Baiadere"

SCHIFF, R. (Germany)
  W.R.B. & Co.

22-74 "Leda & the Swan"	15 - 18	18 - 22
22-74 "Head in Clouds"	12 - 15	15 - 18

SCHIVERT, V. (Germany)
  Arthur Rehn & Co.

"Die Hexe"	20 - 25	25 - 28

SCHMUTZLER, L. (Germany)
  Russian Publisher, Richard

245 "Salome" (Severed Head)	12 - 15	15 - 20

S. SCHNEIDER

Little is known of the artist S. Schneider. His real photo and real photo-type images, mainly of male nudes being confronted by strange and eerie supernatural animals and beings, have become extremely popular with the Fantasy postcard collector.

A large percentage of his works appeared on cards that were issued in Russia, and have divided and undivided Russian backs. However, many also have German, French and bilingual backs for use in other countries. Schneider's works are definitely "stranger-than-fiction" fantasy renditions, and many appear to emit implications of bondage in strange ways. For collectors who search for something different, this type material will be a fascinating change from the normal fare.

SCHNEIDER, S. (Germany)

182 Nude adorned with thorny shoots	30 - 35	35 - 40
1085 Flying man-bull and student		
1088 Supernatural animal, angel, corpse		
Death mourner and huge breasted beast		
1216 Nude with torch & eerie monster		
1235 Nude in chains & eerie monster		
1245 Nude bird-man with slave		

SCHUTZ, ERIC (Austria)
  Poster Cards
  B.K.W.I.

41 "The Frog King" (Big Frog)	18 - 22	22 - 25
885 Goethe's "Der Fischer" (Mermaid)	30 - 35	35 - 40
885 "Der Gott und Der Baiadere"	20 - 25	25 - 30
979 "Die Forelle" (Mermaid)	30 - 35	35 - 40
205 Wagner's "Parsival"	15 - 18	18 - 22
557 "Lotusblume" (Nude in flower)	25 - 30	30 - 35
Series 165 (6) (Nudes on Giant Flowers)	25 - 30	30 - 35

SETKOWICZ

Music, Harp and Snakes	18 - 22	22 - 25

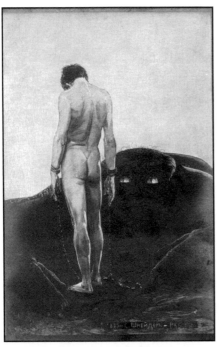

S. Schneider, Russian Publisher
No. 1235

S. Schneider, Russian Publisher
No. 182

S. Schneider, Russian Publisher
No. 1085

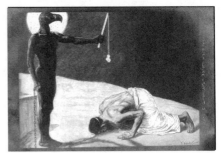

S. Schneider, Russian Publisher
No No.

S. Schneider, Russian Publisher
No. 1245

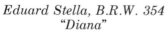

Eduard Stella, B.R.W. 354
"Diana"

P. Szyndler, ANCZYC 22
"Ève"

SIMONSON-CASTELLI, PROF.
  Hans Friedrich

565 Nude and big snake	15 - 18	18 - 22

SOLOMKO, S. (Russia)
  TSN

"The Blue Bird"	15 - 20	20 - 25
"Circe"		
"Dream of Icarius"		
"Fortune Telling"		
"Glow Worm"		
"Phantasy"		
Semi-Nude in Peacock Feathers	18 - 20	20 - 25
"The Tale"		

STANKE, W. (Germany)
  S.W.S.B.

4776 "Das Marchen" Nude with horse	10 - 12	12 - 15
4777 "Das Geheimnis" Nude with horse		

STELLA, EDUARD (Germany)
  B.R.W.

354 "Diana" (Dogs)	18 - 22	22 - 25

STRNAD, JOS.

Anonymous 255 "Nymphe"	12 - 15	15 - 18

STUCK, FRANZ VON (Germany)

	10 - 12	12 - 15

STYKA, JAN (France)
  Lapina
    810 "Good Friends" (Horse)   10 - 12   12 - 15
SZYNDIER, P. (Poland)
  Mal. Polske
    22 "Éve" (Snakes)   20 - 25   25 - 30
THOMAS
    "Leda" Nude and Swan   12 - 15   15 - 18
VEITH, E. (Austria)
  B.K.W.I.
    1101 "Teasing" (Man-Goat)   10 - 12   12 - 15
WACHSMUTH, M.   10 - 12   12 - 14
WARZENIECKI, M.
WILSA
    90 "Une Nouvelle Esclave" (Death)   12 - 15   15 - 18
WOLLNER, H. (Austria)
  B.K.W.I.
    1101 "Sadismus" (Death Head)   12 - 15   15 - 18
ZANDER (Germany)
  S.S.W.B.
    4790 "Sieg der Schonheit" (Tiger)   12 - 15   15 - 18
ZATZKA, H. (The Netherlands)
  Panphot, Vienne
    1284 "La Lerle"
    (Nude in Large Oyster Shell)   15 - 18   18 - 22

ANONYMOUS

Russian
  Real Photo 752 Nude with Snake   18 - 22   22 - 25
  Real Photo No No. Centaur and Nude

TO THE COLLECTORS AND READERS OF THIS PUBLICATION

THIS REFERENCE IS A FIRST EFFORT AND HAS BEEN A TREMENDOUS UNDERTAKING. IT WOULD HAVE BEEN IMPOSSIBLE WITHOUT THE GREAT EFFORT AND CONTRIBUTIONS OF MANY COLLECTORS, DEALERS AND POSTCARD HISTORIANS. WE HOPE THIS BOOK WILL FILL THE NEED FOR COLLECTORS OF FANTASY POSTCARDS; HOWEVER, WE KNOW THAT THE LISTINGS HERE ARE INCOMPLETE. IN ORDER TO MAKE THE SECOND EDITION EVEN MORE COMPREHENSIVE, WE REQUEST THAT YOU SEND US ANY ADDITIONS TO CHECKLISTS OR PUBLISHERS' LISTINGS THAT WE HAVE MISSED.

J. L. MASHBURN, COLONIAL HOUSE
P. O. BOX 609, ENKA, NC 28728 (704-667-1427)

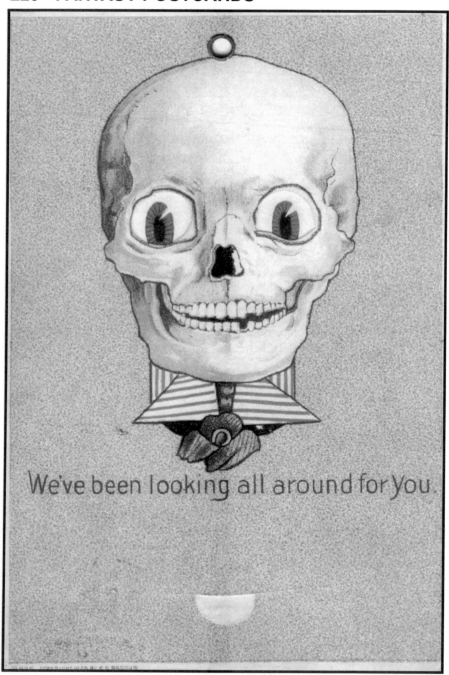

Mechanical Death Head
F. S. Backus, H-695
"We've been looking all around for You."

Chapter 11

Death Fantasy

Death is a process of nature for all mankind and, in that vein, it is certainly not a fantasy. However, some of the events that precede it makes it so. The fears and anguish of growing old, the thoughts of wars and pestilence, and the torment of dying with a deadly, lingering disease all bring fantastic thoughts and dreams which are indeed Death Fantasy.

Death, while feared by many, may be relatively calm and peaceful for those with very little to live for. Death, in myth and literature, has been portrayed by writers and artists as one of the greatest enemies of man. Picture the black-hooded Grim Reaper with his merciless scythe...a skeleton on a black horse with eyes of madness and nostrils flaring...or a smiling death head so sure of his prey...and a cynical, staring death head laughing at the foolish as they drink and revel. These are the epic images in a fantasy world.

Some try to escape or strive to annihilate death by any means; however, by all accounts, he continues to peer over our shoulder and wins in the end. The artists of the great postcard era portrayed death in all the inevitable ways as mentioned above.

Many of the large Death Heads seem to convey a warning of sorts where the various players make up its composition. This composition is much the same as Metamorphics, but Death Heads are definitely a separate entity in the world of fantasy postcards.

DEATH FANTASY

	VG	EX
BALUSCHEK		
"Ghost and Death"	$ 10 - 12	$ 12 - 15
BÖCKLIN, A. (Germany)		
Julius Bard, Berlin		
"Der Kreig"	15 - 18	18 - 22
F. Bruckmann, München		
"Selfportrait mit Tod"		
BURFEL, O. (Germany)		
Death in Black	12 - 15	15 - 20
CIEZKIEWKZ, E.		
"Girl in Red"	12 - 15	15 - 18
"Woman & Skull"		
"Le Nocturne de Chopin"	15 - 18	18 - 20
Girl looks at death		
CHOPIN, FR.		
Series 116 "Playing Death"	10 - 12	12 - 15
CORBELLA, TITO (Italy)		
Uff. Rev. Stampa, Milano Series 268		
Death and Edith Cavell	20 - 25	25 - 28

A. Böcklin, Bruckmann's 1
"Self Portrait with Tod" (Death)

A. Böcklin, A. B., Dresden 204
"Der Krieg"

E. Cieczklewicz, A.F.W. 91
Foreign Caption

A. D. Goltz, B.K.W.I. 1009
"Illusion"

A. Hering, Arthur Rehn & Co.
69, "The Death and the Girl"

F. Keller, Hanfstaengl's 23-1
"Finale"

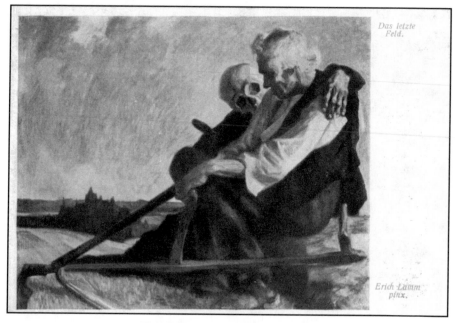

Erich Lamm, B.K.W.I. 1521
"Das letzte Feld"

1 - "Cavell Standing over the Conquered
    Figure of Death ..."
2 - "Death Offering Head of Cavell ..."
3 - "Death and Arrogant German Officer ..."
4 - "Cavell Standing Before Death ..."
5 - "Death Hovers as Cavell Gives Water ..."
6 - "Death Plays Piano as Cavell Lies ..."

ERLANG
    "Die Vision," Nude and Death Head   15 - 18   18 - 22
FAHRENKROG, LUDVIG (Germany)
    Wilhelm Hartung
        104 "Fate"   15 - 18   18 - 22
FISCHER, J. (Czech.)
    Minerva, Prague
        40 "Spectre de la guerre"   15 - 18   18 - 22
GASSNER
    Death on a Black Horse   12 - 15   15 - 20
GOLTZ, A. D. (Germany)
    "Illusion"   12 - 15   15 - 20
HERING, ADOLF (Germany)
    Arthur Rehn & Co.
        "Der Tod and das Madchen"   18 - 22   22 - 25
KELLER, FERDINAND (Germany)
    Franz Hanfstaengl
        "Finale"   12 - 15   15 - 18
JUNG, F.
    Ghost in the swamp   8 - 10   10 - 12

J. Fischer, Minerva 40
"Spectre de la guerre"

KLAKARSCHEVA
    "Ikarus" — 10 - 12   12 - 15

KORPAK, T.
    Ghost and Death — 12 - 15   15 - 20

LAMM, ERICH (Austria)
    B.K.W.I.
        1521 Death in the Field — 10 - 12   12 - 15

LE0PAROVA
    "Fable" — 12 - 15   15 - 18

LIST, FR. (Hungary)
    Series 116/2
        "Rhapsodie Hongroise" — 10 - 12   12 - 15

MANDL, J.
    "The End" — 12 - 15   15 - 18

NEJEDLY
    Salon J.P.P.
        "Inspiration"

PETER, O. (Germany)
    400 Burning Nudes — 12 - 15   15 - 20

PODKOWINSKI (Poland)
    Nude on Fiery Horse — 15 - 18   18 - 22

REASTELLI
    "The Coming Storm" — 12 - 15   15 - 18

WACHSMUTH, M. (Germany)
    P.F.B. in diamond
        "Die Beute" — 12 - 15   15 - 20

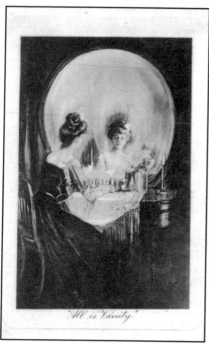

Anonymous, Alfred Schweizer
"All is Vanity"

Real Photo by T.I.C.
"L'amour de Pierrot"

Real Photo, P.F.B. 226
"Lettre d'adieu"

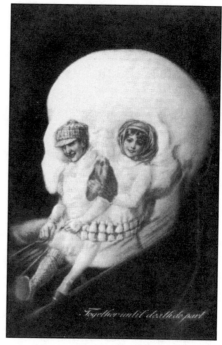

Real Photo, Anonymous
"Together until death do part"

WILFE		
Poster "Der Walschrat"	15 - 18	18 - 22
WOLFF, H. (Germany)		
P.F.B. in diamond		
4480 Death Rides a Horse	12 - 15	15 - 20
WOLLNER, H. (Germany)		
B.K.W.I.		
2402 "Seduction"	15 - 18	18 - 25
PFB, Series 226	15 - 20	20 - 25
Anonymous		
Death Fiddles while Clowns Dance (Und.)	20 - 25	25 - 30

DEATH HEADS

Novitas		
21101 Death Head on car body	18 - 22	22 - 25
21102 Death Head with 2 Drinkers		
Rotophot		
09-585 Death Head; Man-Woman cooking	22 - 25	25 - 28
SB Death Head; Lovers Drinking (6)	18 - 22	22 - 25
Schweizer		
129 Death Head - "All is Vanity"	20 - 22	22 - 25
Real Photos Types		
"L'amour de Pierrot"	25 - 30	30 - 35
PFB 226 "Lettre d'adieu"		
"Napoleon" (2)		
Rarer Publishers	35 - 50	50 - 100

Unsigned S. L. Schmucker
John Winsch © 1911
"Hallowe'en Greetings"

Chapter 12

Halloween

From bats to black cats, from flying witches to maidens fair, from Pumpkin Men to "Goblins will get you if you don't watch out!" Halloween presents to the postcard collector a tremendous variety of wonderful cards from which to choose, and literally all qualify as fantasy in some way. Since all types are collectible, their true fantasy for children and adults alike make them the most desirable of all U.S. holiday postcards. Santas, however, are probably the number one single type.

At least ninety percent of all Halloween cards, and most all of those of the 1900-1915 era, were printed in Germany by the great German lithographers, and were done exclusively for the American trade. Since collectors in other countries have little reason to secure an "American only" holiday card, there is no competition from abroad as there is with Christmas, New Year's, Easter, etc.

For some reason, only a small number of artists signed their Halloween renderings, and inadequate record keeping by publishers has caused most of the works to remain anonymous. The classical J. Winsch cards, illustrating the beautiful works of S. L. Schmucker and, to a lesser degree, those of J. Freixas, are definitely the most sought after of all that were published. Their works were mostly unsigned but have been identified from signed originals.

The card with the highest value is a mechanical card, signed by Ellen H. Clapsaddle, of a little black child dressed in Halloween attire. It is one of a four-card series published by International Art Publishing Co. The other three are of white children. Frances Brundage had many Halloween cards produced by Raphael Tuck and Sam Gabriel, but those published by Gabriel were not among her best works. The most prolific publishers were probably E. Nash and Gibson Art. They had series numbered from one up to the high 40's, with reprintings of various series.

> SINCE THERE ARE A RELATIVELY SMALL NUMBER OF ARTISTS, WE ARE LISTING THE PUBLISHER FIRST IN THIS CHAPTER. THE ARTIST IS LISTED IN EACH SERIES UNDER EACH PUBLISHER.

HALLOWEEN

	VG	EX
AA (Anglo American)		
Series 876 (6) Witch Series	$ 12 - 15	$ 15 - 18
AMERICAN POST CARD CO.		
Series 143 (6) Glamorous Witch Ladies		

F. Brundage, Sam Gabriel 123
"Hallowe'en Greetings."

F. Brundage, Sam Gabriel 120
"Hallowe'en Greetings."

2413 "Hallowe'en Greeting"	20 - 25	25 - 28
Others		
ANNIN & CO.	8 - 10	10 - 12
AMP CO.	10 - 12	12 - 15
A.P.M. CO., Series 303	12 - 15	15 - 18
AUBURN POSTCARD CO.		
Series 116 (10 or 12?)	8 - 10	10 - 12
S/H.W.A.		
Series 2500	8 - 10	10 - 12
S/E. Weaver		
Series 2335, 2399 (8)	8 - 10	10 - 12
B.B., LONDON (Birn Bros.)		
Series E59 (6)	12 - 15	15 - 18
B.W. Series 374 (12)	12 - 15	15 - 20
BAMBERGER, FLORENCE (Signed by)	10 - 12	12 - 15
BANKS, E. C. (Signed by) See Langsdorf & Co.		
BARTON & SPOONER (BS)		
Series 7146	10 - 12	12 - 15
S. BERGMAN CO.		
Series 321, 322, 323 (4)	10 - 12	12 - 15
Series 1623, 1690, 3136 (6)		
Series 6026, 6069, 6070, 6071 (6)		
Series 7035, 9029 (6)		
Series 9033, 9076, 9086 (6)		
Series 9104, 9120 (6)		
S/E. Von H.		
Series 6026, 6027	12 - 15	15 - 18
S/Bernhardt Wall		
Series 9101	12 - 15	15 - 18
No No. Cat Series (6)	15 - 18	18 - 22
No No. Children Series (6)	12 - 15	15 - 18
A. C. BOSSELMAN	12 - 15	15 - 18
JULIUS BIEN & CO.		
Series 980 (6)	15 - 18	18 - 22
Others		
CHARLES S. CLARK CO.		
S/MHS		
Series 122 (6)	15 - 18	18 - 22
R. L. CONWELL CO.		
Series 247 (6)	12 - 15	15 - 18
Series 630 (6)	15 - 18	18 - 22
A.M. DAVIS Co.		
S/AEH		
Series 657 (12)	18 - 22	22 - 25
S/P		
Series 658 (12)	15 - 18	18 - 22
FAIRMAN CO. (Pink of Perfection) *		
Series 152, 153, 400, 402, 606	10 - 12	12 - 15

S. Bergman, 6026
"Happy Hallowe'en!"

Anonymous, Series 2097
"All Hallowe'en Greetings."

Anonymous, Series 37
"A Halloween Spell"

Anonymous, 778
"A Happy Hallowe'en"

Series 6908, 6929, 6931, 6932, 6947, 6948	8 - 10	10 - 12
S/Kathryn Elliott (B&W)		
S/Bernhardt Wall (B&W)		
*Many designs are same as Gibson Art Co.		

SAM GABRIEL or GABRIEL & SONS
S/Frances Brundage

Series 120, 121 (10)	20 - 22	22 - 25
Series 123 (10)	12 - 15	15 - 18
Series 125 (6)		

S/M La F R (Mary La Fentra Russell)

Series 124 (6)	10 - 12	12 - 15

Cards with Felt Attachments - Add $5.00

S. GARRE
S/Ellen H. Clapsaddle
No No. Series (6)

"Would You Believe It?"	18 - 22	22 - 25

GARTNER & BENDER

No No. Children Series (B&W)	10 - 12	12 - 15
No No. Ladies Series (B&W)		
S/M. Ries (B&W)	8 - 10	10 - 12

GIBSON ART

Series 606 Children	12 - 15	15 - 18
Kathryn Elliott, Sepia (12+)	8 - 10	10 - 12
Bernhardt Wall, Sepia (12)		
Many other unnumbered Series:		
Over 40 different Sets or Series	8 - 10	10 - 18

GOTTSCHALK, DREYFUSS & DAVIS *

Series 2399, 2401, 2402, 2470, 2471 (4)	15 - 18	18 - 22
Series 2504, 2516, 2525, 2526, 2662 (4)		
Series 2693, 2696 (4)		

* Cards are both embossed and Gel types.
   Gel types are not as popular because of
   cracking surfaces.

Series 5049, 5050 (4) (Flat printing)	12 - 15	15 - 18

Girl/mailbox symbol (possibly GD&S) *

Series 2040 & 2040A, 2041 (12 each)	15 - 18	18 - 22
Series 2097, 2171, 2243 (12)		
Series 2276, 2279, 2402, 2470 (6)		

* Some have **B. Hoffman** copyright, 1909.

HENDERSON LITHO CO.

H Series	12 - 15	15 - 18

INTERNATIONAL ART MFG. CO.

Series 1908 (6)	12 - 15	15 - 18

S/AEB

No No. Series	10 - 12	12 - 15

Ellen H. Clapsaddle

No. No. (12)	15 - 18	18 - 22
Series 501 (4)	20 - 30	30 - 40
Series 978 (6)	15 - 18	18 - 22

E. H. Clapsaddle, S. Garre
"Would You Believe It!"

E. H. Clapsaddle, Int. Art Co.
978 "A Thrilling Hallowe'en"

Series 1236 Mechanicals (4)		
White Children (3)	200 - 250	250 - 275
Black Child (1)	400 - 450	450 - 500
Series 1237, 1238 (4)	15 - 18	18 - 22
Series 1301 (12)	50 - 60	60 - 75
Series 1393 (6)	15 - 18	18 - 22
Series 1667 (12)	12 - 15	15 - 18
Series 1815 (6) (Uns.)	10 - 12	12 - 15
Series 4439 (6)	15 - 18	18 - 22
Aleinmuller		
Series 1002 (6)	12 - 15	15 - 18
Bernhardt Wall		
No No. (12)	12 - 15	15 - 18
Others		
Series 4439 (6)	10 - 12	12 - 15
M. L. JACKSON (Signed by)		
"Don'ts" Series	12 - 15	15 - 18
L & E		
HBG (H. B. Griggs)		
Series 2214, 2215, 2216 (4)	12 - 15	15 - 18
Series 2229 (4) (Uns.)	20 - 22	22 - 25
Series E2231, 2262, 2272, 4010 (12)	12 - 15	15 - 18
Series 7018, 7027, 7036 (12) (Uns.)	10 - 12	12 - 15

*Rare Clapsaddle Mechanical
International Art Series 1236*

*Rare Clapsaddle Mechanical
International Art Series 1236*

*Unsigned Ellen Clapsaddle
Wolf & Co. Series 501*

*Ellen Clapsaddle
International Art Series 1301*

E. H. Clapsaddle, Int. Art Co.
1237, "A Happy Hallowe'en"

DWIG, J. Marks 981
"The Way To Fly Is With Your..."

HBG (H. B. Griggs), L. & E. 2262
"Could I Borrow a Witches Flying-Machine I'd Visit You ..."

E. Nash, H-16
"Hallowe'en"

E. Nash, 6
"Listen, Little One!"

S. LANGSDORF & CO.
    No No. Gel finish (12)   10 - 12   12 - 15
    S/E.C. Banks (Ghosts and Witches) (4?)   15 - 18   18 - 22
    S/E.C. Banks (Red Borders) (8) 5 signed
R. H. L. (Robert H. Lord) (Signed by)   10 - 12   12 - 15
FRED LOUNSBURY CO., Series 2052 (4)   12 - 15   15 - 18
MANHATTAN PUB. CO. (Pen & Ink T.M.)
    Series 1135 (5)   10 - 12   12 - 15
J. MARKS, Series 980 (6)   15 - 18   18 - 22
    S/Dwig (Clare Victor Dwiggins) (Uns.)
        Series 981 (6)
        "And All Girls Know The Way to Fly..."   25 - 30   30 - 35
        "And All Pretty Girls are Witches"
        "Come Fly With Me..."
        "I'll Be Your Pumpkin If..."
        "Now All Good Witches..."
        "Oh Won't You Come Play Witch With Me"
METROPOLITAN NEWS CO. (M in Bean Pot)
    Series 1133, 1134, 1135, 1275, 1276 (6)   10 - 12   12 - 15
E. NASH
    Series 1, 2, 3, 4, 5, and 6 (6)   12 - 15   15 - 18
    Series 6, H-6 through 28, H-28 *
    Series H-12   15 - 18   18 - 22
   * Have Copyright T.M. and N in Triangle
    Series 29, H-29 through H-49 (4 & 6)   12 - 15   15 - 18

P. Sander, No No.
"Halloween Greetings"

Santway 140
"Hallowe'en Brigade

Series **H-425 - H-430** are reprints	12 - 15	15 - 18
NATIONAL ART CO.		
S/Archie Gunn		
216 "Jack-o-Lantern"	22 - 25	25 - 28
NATIONAL ART PUB. CO., Series 70 (4)	12 - 15	15 - 18
F. A. OWEN	6 - 8	8 - 10
OUTCAULT, R. (Signed by)		
Buster Brown Calendars (Adv.)	40 - 50	50 - 75
P.F.B. (Paul Finkenrath, Berlin)		
Series 778 (6)	20 - 25	25 - 28
Series 9422 (6) Same as Series 778		
G. K. PRINCE, S/M.M.S.	10 - 12	12 - 15
H. I. ROBBINS		
Series 142 (12)	10 - 12	12 - 15
Series 363		
Series 383 (12?) Same as Series 142		
THE ROSE CO.	8 - 10	10 - 12
RUST CRAFT SHOP	10 - 12	12 - 15
SAS CO.		
Series 300, 301, 302 (4)	10 - 12	12 - 15
Series 351, 352 (4)		
SB		
Bernhardt Wall (Uns.), **Series 7151**	18 - 22	22 - 25
SAMSON BROS.		
Series 34A, L34 (3) Then reversed (6)	10 - 12	12 - 15

Stecher Litho, Series 226
"Hallowe'en Pranks"

Stecher Litho, Series 226
"Hallowe'en Pleasures"

M. W. Taggart, Series 804
"The Mysteries of Halloween"

R. Tuck & Sons "Hallowe'en" Series 150
"Hallowe'en"

Series S500, L500 (3) Then reversed (6)		
Series 600, 601 (6) various colors		
Series 619 (6)	12 - 15	15 - 18
Series S640 (3) Then reversed (6)		
Series CS657, CS658 (6)		
Series 1312 (6)		
Series 1316 (6 Same 1312		
Series 7107, 7107A, 7107B (6)		
Series 7146 (6) Same as 7107		
Series 7151 (6)		
Series 7151B (6)	10 - 12	12 - 15
P. SANDER		
S/Clare Angell		
No No. (6) (B&W)	10 - 12	12 - 15
S/Bernhardt Wall		
Series 240 (4 or 6?)		
Series 366 (6)	8 - 10	10 - 12
Others		
Series 581 (6)	10 - 12	12 - 15
No No.	10 - 12	12 - 15
SANFORD CARD CO.		
S/ABC	8 - 10	10 - 12
S/AMC		
SANTWAY (S in diamond)		
Series 140 (6)	10 - 12	12 - 15
STECHER LITHO CO.		
Uns./J.E.P. (James E. Pitts) J.E.P. in logo		

Series 57 (6)	15 - 18	18 - 22
Series 63 (6)		

S/M.E.P. (Margaret E. Price)

Series 400 (6) (2 signed M.P.)	15 - 18	18 - 22
Series 419 (6) (Signed M.P.) Flat printed		
Series 1239 (4) (Uns.) Flat printed	10 - 12	12 - 15

Others

Series 80, 90, 216, 226, 332 (6)	15 - 18	18 - 22
Series 339 (6)	10 - 12	12 - 15
Series 345, 408 (6)	15 - 18	18 - 22
Series 248 (6) Mirror Series		
Series 1238, 1290, 1291 (4) Flat printed	8 - 10	10 - 12

T. P. & CO.   (Taylor-Platt Co.)

Series 866	6 - 8	8 - 10

M. W. TAGGART

Series 803 (8)	12 - 15	15 - 18
Series 804 (8) Same as 803 but reversed		

TAYLOR ART	15 - 18	18 - 20

TOWER CO.

Series 103S (6)	6 - 8	8 - 10

RAPHAEL TUCK

S. L. Schmucker (Uns.)

Series 100 (9 known)

Girl dressed in sheet, many JOL's	125 - 150	150 - 175

"Bats and owls and witch-y capers..."
Girl pixie dressed in black, 3 JOL's
"Hallowe'en Greetings"
Girl with cape and Japanese lanterns
"Hallowe'en Wishes"
Girl with mask, 5 big masks behind
"This maid will mask on Hallowe'en"
Boy with Japanese lanterns, big moon
"Sing a Song of Hallowe'en"
Girl wears checked dress and JOL man
"This maiden here is dancing with..."
Girl wears JOL cloak, with JOL on stick
"Were you this maid on Hallowe'en"
Girl dressed as clown, JOL on a stick
"Witches, Fay's and Sprites unseen..."
Boy with flute sits on big JOL
"When you're away on Hallowe'en"

Series 150, 183 (12)	10 - 12	12 - 15
Series 160 (12), 190 (10)	15 - 18	18 - 20

Frances Brundage (Uns.)

Series 174 (6)	20 - 25	25 - 28
Series 184 (12)	18 - 22	22 - 25
C.B.T., Series 181 (10)	12 - 14	14 - 16

E.M.H.

Series 197 (10)	20 - 22	22 - 25

R. Tuck Series 100
"This maiden here is dancing..."

R. Tuck Series 100
"Were you this maid on Hallo..."

Grace Wiederseim/Drayton (Uns.)

Series 807 (4)		
"Hallowe'en. Look in the glass..."	80 - 90	90 - 100
"Jack O'Lantern"		
"O-o-o - The Witches Brew"		
"The Witch!"		
Others		
Series 183, 190 (10) **816**	10 - 12	12 - 15
Series 803		
Series 188 (10)	15 - 18	18 - 22
Series 830, 831 (3)	10 - 12	12 - 15
ULLMAN MFG. CO.		
No No. (B&W)	8 - 10	10 - 12
No No. (8) (Color)	10 - 12	12 - 14
Series 143, 182 (7)	10 - 12	12 - 15
S/Bernhardt Wall	15 - 20	20 - 30
VALENTINE & SONS	10 - 12	12 - 15
Signed and Unsigned Bernhardt Wall	20 - 30	30 - 40
P. F. VOLLAND & CO.		
Series numbered 4041-4048	15 - 18	18 - 22
E. WEAVER (Signed by) See Auburn P.C. Co.		
Series 2335, 2399 (8)	8 - 10	10 - 12
GEORGE C. WHITNEY	12 - 15	15 - 18
S. L. Schmucker (Uns.)		

*Uns. Schmucker, Whitney Made
"May you be jolly and gay..."*

*Uns. Schmucker, Whitney Stand-
up, "Hallowe'en Greetings to You"*

Stand-up type

Boy and girl with lantern, green imps	100 - 110	110 - 125
"Be brave and bold on Hallowe'en..."		
Three children, pumpkins, owl, JOL		
"Hallowe'en Greetings to You"		
Three children with clown on a stick		
"Just a wish for a Happy Hallowe'en"		
Dutch boy, girl in flowered dress, goblins		
"May you be Jolly and Gay..."		
Two girls watch flying witch, big moon		
"On Hallowe'en watch and you may..."		
Boy and girl meet big vegetable man		
"Since I am here and you are there..."		
Hallowe'en Fold-outs	100 - 125	125 - 150
Others		
Large Images	20 - 22	22 - 25
Small Images	15 - 18	18 - 20
Animated Pumpkins	20 - 22	22 - 25
Party Invitations	15 - 18	18 - 22

JOHN WINSCH

  S. L. Schmucker (Uns.)

Copyright, 1911 - Vertical * (6)		
Head & shoulders of blonde, black hood	75 - 100	100 - 125
"A Happy Hallowe'en"		

Winsch © 1914 Variety
Unknown Artist, Reduced Design

Winsch © 1914 Variety
Unknown Artist, Reduced Design

Winsch © 1912
Unknown Artist

S. L. Schmucker, Winsch © 1913
"Hallowe'en Faces!"

Winsch © 1914 Variety
Unknown Artist, Reduced Design

Winsch © 1914 Variety
Unknown Artist, Reduced Design

Winsch © 1915 Variety
Unknown Artist, Reduced Design

S. L. Schmucker-Jason Freixas Combined Work
John Winsch, No Copyright, "A Starry Hallowe'en"

Lady riding broom, moon behind
    "All Hallowe'en"
Lady in long white hooded robe
    "On Hallowe'en"
Lady in red dress, owl on head
    "Hallowe'en Greeting"
Lady in black evening gown
    "Greeting at Hallowe'en"
Lady asleep, 3 fairies "Hallowe'en Time"

* 3 different sets of variations of 1911   125 - 200   200 - 400
series show smaller same design images
but with different captions
Copyright, 1912 - Vertical * (6)
Lady witch in front of big cauldron   75 - 100   100 - 125
    "The Hallowe'en Cauldron"
Lady in black, leering moon behind
    "The Hallowe'en Lantern"
Lady in white-hooded cape, JOL's
    "The Magic Hallowe'en"
Lady in red elfin costume
    "The Hallowe'en Witch's Wand"
Lady in white clown suit, owls
    "A Hallowe'en Morning"
Lady in green dress, JOL man
    "A Hallowe'en Wish"

Unsigned J. Freixas/S. L. Schmucker Combinations

*	4 different sets of variations of 1912 series (one same size images and 3 smaller; 3 are copyrighted; 2 are vertical and 2 are horizontal)	125 - 200	200 - 300
	Copyright, 1913 "Mask" Ser. Hor. * (4)		
	Clown in red and Jack-in-the Box "Hallowe'en Surprises"	150 - 175	175 - 225
	Witch and clown hold jump rope "Hallowe'en Bambols!"		
	Woman in long white hooded robe "Hallowe'en Faces"		
	Girl in white dress, huge masks "Hallowe'en Faces"		
*	One other set of variation of 1913 series has embossed design, black/gold stars border, different captions and cards	200 - 250	250 - 350
	are not copyrighted (#4972 on reverse)	100 - 125	125 - 150
	Copyright, 1913 - Horizontal * (4)		
	Girl in white dress "A Starry Hallowe'en"	75 - 100	100 - 125
	Girl in dotted dress sits on pumpkin "Hallowe'en Night"		
	Boy surrounded by big JOL's "Hallowe'en Pumpkins"		
	Girl in white between owl and vegetable "Hallowe'en Jollity"		
*	4 other sets of variations of 1913 series and all are copyrighted 1913		

Winsch combined the works of S. L. Schmucker and Jason Freixas on a number of variations and reduced designs. This combination is illustrated in the "Mask-(Schmucker) Child-(Freixas)" on the photo with checkered border entitled "A Starry Hallowe'en." These cards now bring a premium above those of non-combined issues.

1912 German, Unsigned (6) *	60 - 75	75 - 90
Smaller variations, reduced design	90 - 100	100 - 140
1913 German, Unsigned	60 - 80	80 - 90
Smaller variations, reduced design	90 - 100	100 - 140
1914 German, Unsigned	60 - 80	80 - 90
Smaller variations, reduced design	90 - 100	100 - 140
1914, Copyright, Children, Uns./J. Freixas	70 - 80	80 - 90
Variations	70 - 80	80 - 90
1914, Copyright, Unsigned Witches, owls	65 - 75	75 - 95
Variations	50 - 60	60 - 70
1915, Copyright, Children, Uns./Freixas		
and other artists	100 - 120	120 - 140
Black Checkered Border, no copyright		
Uns./Freixas	90 - 100	100 - 125
Orange Border, Children, no copyright	200 - 250	250 - 300
Schmucker-Freixas card, no copyright		
Boy with mask scares girl (Unsigned)	250 - 300	300 - 350
Series 4975, No copyright, cats, goblins (4)	50 - 60	60 - 70
* Add $25-30 for Schmucker-Freixas		
combined images.		
WOLF & CO.		
S/Ellen H. Clapsaddle		
Series 1	15 - 18	18 - 22
Series 31 (18?)	15 -18	18 - 22
Series 501 (6)	40 - 50	50 - 60
All Black & Orange Background		
H. L. WOHLER	15 - 18	18 - 22
A.A. ZWIEBEL, Wilkes Barre		
Children frolics (2 known)	80 - 90	90 - 100
ANONYMOUS PUBLISHERS		
Series B37, 38, 142, 160	12 - 15	15 - 18
Series 303, 304, 308, 363, 374		
Series 552 (6) (Emb.)	25 - 28	28 - 32
Series 0624	10 - 12	12 - 15
Series 876, 1026, 1028		
Series 914		
Series 1015, 1035	12 - 15	15 - 18
Blacks on Hallowe'en		
Card No. 6505 "You would laugh too..."	30 - 35	35 - 50
Card No. 6508 "Strange sights are seen..."		
REAL PHOTOS		
Children in Costumes	Range	50 - 200
Adults in Costumes	Range	75 - 200
Halloween Parties	Range	40 - 150

A Classic H-T-L of Dressed Easter Bunny with Children

Chapter 13

Hold-to-Light

Die-cut hold-to-light and transparency postcards, especially those of Santa Claus and dressed animals, are the highlight of any Fantasy postcard collection. Produced in Europe for both the European and the American markets, they are extremely beautiful, extremely rare, and very hard to find. Also, prices have risen dramatically for all in undamaged condition.

The most popular are the die-cut versions which have several layers of paper. The portions to be illuminated are removed, leaving a very thin layer nearest the back and one in front for strength. The former contains painted colors for desired effects, and when held to a strong light these beautiful colors show through. Transparencies also have several layers of paper, but the front layer is very thin. The second layer contains the design which can be seen when held to a light. Transparencies are valued at approximately one-half the values of the more popular die-cuts.

Santa die-cuts are the elite group and have the highest values. The large full-figures are now in the $200-$300 range, with those signed by the German artist Mailick being the most popular and in greatest demand. The highest priced, however, are the extremely rare Uncle Sam Santas (made only for the U.S. market) which range from $2,000 to $3,400 each. Santa transparencies are valued from $75 to $150.

Dressed animals of the various holidays are also in great demand. The leaders in this area are the very scarce issues of dressed

Thanksgiving turkeys or those doing people things. Since Thanksgiving is strictly an American holiday, smaller numbers were printed which was not the case for other holidays. Easter cards of dressed bunnies, Valentines of colorful cupids, Christmas angels and cherubs, snowmen, pigs and year dates, and fairy tales round out this wonderful fantasy group. There were no Halloween HTL's. This is very disappointing as many feel that they would have made the most beautiful and colorful of all the holiday cards.

Hold-to-Lights were usually published in sets containing four cards; however, there were many variations of the originals. Although there are numbers applied to many cards, these apparently do not mean anything relating to series or sets. The principal publisher was D.R.G.M., Germany. Most cards, however, have no publisher byline or have the notation "Printed in Germany."

HOLD-TO-LIGHT

	VG	EX
FAIRY TALES		
Transparencies	$ 40 - 50	$ 50 - 75
MAIKAFIRS (May Bugs)	40 - 50	50 - 60
Transparencies	30 - 35	35 - 40
NEW YEAR'S		
Snowmen		
Large	50 - 60	60 - 70
Small	40 - 50	50 - 60
S/Mailick	60 - 70	70 - 80
Year Dates	35 - 40	40 - 50
Figures made of children	40 - 50	50 - 60
Figures made of pigs	50 - 60	60 - 75
Figures made of snowmen	60 - 75	75 - 100
Unsigned Children of Frances Brundage	50 - 60	60 - 75
VALENTINE'S DAY		
Cupids	50 - 60	60 - 75
EASTER		
Angels	30 - 40	40 - 50
S/Mailick	70 - 80	80 - 90
Bunnies	60 - 70	70 - 80
Bunnies/Children		
Chicks	40 - 50	50 - 60
Children in Easter Eggs	50 - 60	60 - 70

Valentine Cupid   *Easter Dressed Bunnies*

THANKSGIVING

Turkeys	75 - 100	100 - 125
Children/Big Turkeys	150 - 175	175 - 200

CHRISTMAS

Angels	50 - 60	60 - 70
W/Christmas trees	65 - 70	70 - 75
S/Mailick	70 - 80	80 - 100
Cherubs	40 - 50	50 - 60
Santas		
Large Santas, Robes other than red	250 - 300	300 - 400
Small Santas	150 - 200	200 - 250
Santas in red robes	150 - 175	175 - 250
S/Mailick (4, with variations)		
D.R.G.M.	200 - 250	250 - 400
Transparencies	75 - 100	100 - 125
Uncle Sam Santas (4)		
a. Santa knocking on door	2750 - 3200	3200 - 3800
b. Santa trimming tree		
c. Santa standing on step		
d. Santa at window with bag of toys	3200 - 3500	3500 - 4200
Turkeys	75 - 100	100 - 125
Turkeys/Children	150 - 175	175 - 200

Easter Dressed Bunny with Child

Child in Easter Egg

Child in Easter Egg

*German Chromo-Lithograph
New Year*

*German Chromo-Lithograph
New Year*

*Mailick
Anonymous German Publisher*

Christmas Angel with Tree

Christmas Angel with Tree

Christmas Angel with Tree

Christmas Angel with Tree

Christmas Angel with Tree

Christmas Angel with Tree

Christmas Angel

Easter Angel

Easter Dressed Bunny

Easter Dressed Bunnies

Easter Dressed Bunny

Easter Dressed Bunnies

*Uncle Sam Santa
Standing on Step*

*Uncle Sam Santa
Trimming Tree*

Christmas Angel with Tree

Large Santa in Purple Robe

Snowman with Children

Christmas Turkey and Child

Thanksgiving Turkey and Child

Thanksgiving Turkey and Child
Note: Thanksgiving Shield

Christmas Turkey and Child
Note: Christmas Shield

New Year
Year Date with Snowmen

Christmas Turkey and Child

New Year
Year Date with Snowmen

Christmas Turkey and Child

Christmas Angel with Tree and Children

Large Santa in Purple Robe
D.R.G.M.

Large Santa in Brown Robe

F.B. (Fritz Baumgarten), Meissner & Buch 3016
"Glückliche Stunden im neuen Jahre"

Chapter 14

Miscellaneous

Fantasy types not listed in the previous chapters are grouped in this special miscellaneous section. In many instances, only one or more samples of a category or motif, be it anonymous, artist-signed, or with a publisher byline, may be listed. Approximate values of others of the same motif may be interpreted from these listings. The exceptions would be special works by more famous artists or those of a special set or series.

Cards listed here are usually uncommon and values will be higher than some of the very common types. Fantasy cupids, for instance, were the motif of hundreds of different Valentines, and most are very common with values of up to $3.00 each. However, certain cupid images, as in the case of the beautiful series by S. L. Schmucker, may be valued up to $50 or more. This is also true for other listings where type of card, publisher, or artist will be the determining factors in valuing a card or series of cards. Cheap, comical images, many of which have definite fantasy overtones but with little collector interest, have been omitted from this work.

Some of the most delightful and interesting fantasy cards, from angels to witches and butterfly ladies to gallant Pierrots, from gnomes and mushroom people to Loreley, the Siren of the Rhine, are listed and pictured here.

Have a wonderful Fantasy time!

MISCELLANEOUS FANTASY

ANGELS

	VG	EX
CLAPSADDLE, ELLEN (U.S.)		
International Art		
Series 1911 (6)	$ 10 - 12	$ 12 - 15
Other Series	6 - 8	8 - 10
KIRCHNER, RAPHAEL (Austria)		
Theo. Stroefer		
Christmas Angels (6)	80 - 90	90 - 100
MAILICK, A. (Germany)		
Easter Angels	15 - 20	20 - 25
Christmas Angels	25 - 30	30 - 35
PUBLISHERS *		
A. M. & B.		
Series 535 (6)	10 - 12	12 - 15
B.W. (Emb.)		
EAS (Emb.)		
M&B (Emb.)		
P.F.B.		
Series 3730, 5000 (6)	12 - 15	15 - 18

Raphael Kirchner, Theo. Stroefer
Christmas Angel Series

Mailick, G. Schutz
"A Merry Christmas"

Mailick, "Erika" 483
"Fröliche Weihnachten"

Raphael Tuck	6 - 8	8 - 10
Other German Publishers		
* Add $2-3 for Angels with Christmas tree.		
Hold-to-Light	35 - 45	45 - 55
S/Mailick		
Christmas	70 - 80	80 - 100
Easter	70 - 80	80 - 90
Faith, Hope, Charity		
A.S.B.		
Series 178 (Emb.)	10 - 12	12 - 15
GB Co. (Emb.)	8 - 10	10 - 12
S. Langsdorf (Emb.)	10 - 12	12 - 15
P.F.B., Series 9103 (6 of 24)	10 - 12	12 - 15
R. Tuck, Series 178	10 - 12	12 - 15
Guardian Angels		
A.S.B.		
Series 250 (6)		
Guards children on railroad tracks	15 - 18	18 - 22
Guards children on fishing pier		
Guards girl with hoop on car tracks		
Series 636 (6)		
Series 3476 (6)		
Birn Bros. (B.B., London)		
Series 2109 (6)	12 - 15	15 - 18

Aircraft over Cities
Fake Photography

Mark Emege		
Series 178 (6)	12 - 15	15 - 18
P.F.B.		
Series 8618 (6)	18 - 22	22 - 25
Guards boy/girl picking flowers		
Guards sleeping children, fire outside		
Series 8621 (6)		
Anonymous		
Series 250	10 - 12	12 - 15
Series 636		
Series 1347 (6)		
Series 1966 (6)		
Series 4059 (6)		

ANTHROPOMORPHIC

(Ascribing human attributes to things not human.)

REG, M.		
Regent Publishing Co.		
Series 2788, Thermometer Man	15 - 20	20 - 25
B. B., London		
Series X-117, Spool of thread man	15 - 20	20 - 25
Series E-103, Pipe and cigar men		
Series E-121, Nut man		

Reg M., Regent Pub. Co. 2788
"I Feel Several Degrees..."

Anonymous, B. B. London E-103
"When you're tired of smoking..."

Anonymous, B. B. London X-117
"To wish you a DARNED fine..."

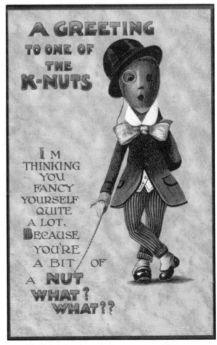

Anonymous, B. B. London E-121
"A Greeting to one of the K-Nuts"

The "Butterfly" Series
By
S. L. Schmucker (Unsigned)
Published by Detroit Publishing Company © 1907

"Beauty"
Girl in Blue

"Elusoriness"
Girl in Yellow

"Fragility"
Girl in Blue-Green

"Inconstancy"
Girl in Red

"L'Envoi"
Girl in Gray

"Sensibility"
Girl in Pink

Advertising
      Michelin Tire Man   80 - 90   90 - 100
Others   30 - 40   40 - 50

AUTO FANTASY

CLAPSADDLE, ELLEN (Uns.)
    International Art
        Blacks in car with watermelon wheels, etc.   30 - 35   35 - 40
        Others   10 - 12   12 - 15
Other Publishers   8 - 10   10 - 12

AUTOS FLYING OVER CITY   12 - 15   15 - 18
    Staged Real Photo types   18 - 22   22 - 25
    Cars of the future types   10 - 12   12 - 15
    Others

BABIES, MULTIPLE

    B.K.W.I. Real Photo Series   12 - 15   15 - 18
        Series 810 (6)   10 - 12   12 - 15
    E. C. Kropp   8 - 10   10 - 12
    K.V.i.B.   10 - 12   12 - 15
    P.F.B., Series 5511 (6)   12 - 15   15 - 18
    Many Others   8 - 10   10 - 12

BUTTERFLIES

ANICHINI, EZIO (Italy)
    Ballerini & Fratini
        Series 351 Butterfly Ladies (4)   20 - 25   25 - 28
CHIOSTRI, SOFIA (Italy)
    Ballerini and Fratini
        Series 310 Children Butterflies (4)   22 - 25   25 - 28
        Series 347 Flying Children (4)
GIRIS, CESAR (Italy)
    R. Tuck
        Series 2365 (6) Butterfly Ladies   25 - 30   30 - 35
ROBRA
    KVB
        Series 3366 (6) (silhouettes)   20 - 25   25 - 28
SCHMUCKER, S. L. (U.S.)
    Detroit Publishing Co., 1907
        "Butterfly" Series (6)
        "Beauty" - Girl in blue   200 - 225   225 - 250
        "Elusoriness" - Girl in yellow
        "Fragility" - Girl in blue-green

Chiostri, Ballerini & Fratini 310
"Priecigus Lieldinas svetkus!"

Robra, KVB 3366
No Caption

Steen, Weenenk & Snel Baarn
"Vrolÿk Kerstfeest"

Anonymous, B.K.W.I. 901-4
Chanticleer Type

"Inconstancy" - Girl in Red (Pictured on Cover)
"LEnvoi" - Girl in gray
"Sensibility" - Girl in pink

USABAL, LOTTE   (Germany)

R & K Series 363 Butterfly Ladies (6)	22 - 25	25 - 28
Other Artists and Publishers	10 - 12	12 - 15

CANDLES

STEEN
   W.S.B.

No No. "Volÿk Kerstfeest"	15 - 18	18 - 22

PUBLISHERS
   Anonymous

Series 532 Candles with Faces	12 - 15	15 - 18

CHANTICLEER   (Human Chickens)

ROSTAND, EDWIN   (France)
   G.L.P.

"Costumes Chanticleer"	10 - 15	15 - 20

Anonymous
   The "Sha'n't tickle 'er" Series

"The Dollar Princess"	12 - 15	15 - 18
Others		
"A Hot Bird and a cold Bottle"	10 - 12	12 - 15

Mailick, WW 4918
"Prosit Neujahr"

Krenes, B.K.W.I. 3172-1
"Prosit Neujahr!"

Anonymous, 09
"Prosit Neujahr!"

M.S.i.B. 13556
"Herzlichen Glückwursch zum ..."

Real Photos

N.G.T. Series 1910	12 - 15	15 - 18
Other French Series	15 - 18	18 - 22
Hand-made Stamp Montage, French	18 - 22	22 - 25

CHERUBS

PFB

Series 3315 (6)	6 - 8	8 - 10
John Winsch, 1911	8 - 10	10 - 12
Many other publishers	2 - 3	3 - 6
Hold-To-Light (See H-T-L Section)		

CHIMNEY SWEEPS

A Chimney Sweep is a man or boy who climbs up chimneys to clean out accumulated soot. In earlier times, "sweeps" made a living by plying this trade in Europe and North America. They were usually painted by postcard artists as young boys (or girls) in fine black suits and top hats with a rooftop and big chimney in the background. They are always shown with a big cleaning brush at the end of a long handle or wire.

As can be imagined this is a very dirty job, and at the end of a long day they were usually covered with soot from head to toe. Artists of those times compared them with lowly pigs because they were so dirty. For this reason many cards show them in the company of a pig, and some go even further and dress pigs as Chimney Sweeps.

A.H. (Austria)	15 - 18	18 - 22
F.B. (Fritz Baumgarten) (Germany)		
Meissner & Buch		
Series 166 (6)	15 - 18	18 - 22
FEIERTAG, KARL (Austria)		
B.K.W.I.		
Series 2930 (6) Chimney Sweeps and Pigs	12 - 15	15 - 18
FIALKOWSKA, WALLY (Austria)		
GROSSMAN, O.	15 - 18	18 - 22
H.M. (Austria)		
HAGER, R. A. (Austria)		
M. Munk, Wien		
Series 1117 (6)	18 - 22	22 - 25
KRATKI, R. (Austria)		
Series 276 (6)	15 - 18	18 - 22
KRENES (Austria)		
B.K.W.I.		

Anonymous
B. Dondorf, Series 285

Anonymous
B. Dondorf, Series 285

B. Wall, P. Sander
"Tom Phoolery, Esq."

C was a Clown who had plenty to say.

Anonymous, P. P. & P. Co.
"C was a Clown who had ..."

Series 3172
1 "Prosit Neujahr!" Lady Chimney Sweep   25 - 28   28 - 32
MAILICK, A. (Germany)
W.W.
    4918 Chromolitho   25 - 28   28 - 32
    With Pig   20 - 25   25 - 30
PATEK, AUGUST (Austria)
Joseph Gurstmayer
    Snow-man Chimney Sweep, Children   20 - 25   25 - 28
PATZ, M. (Austria)   12 - 15   15 - 18
RECKZIEGEL, E. (Austria) C.W. with pigs   15 - 18   18 - 22
PUBLISHERS
    A.K.i.W., Series 2226 (6)   10 - 12   12 - 15
    Amag, Series 2709 (6)   15 - 18   18 - 22
    B.C.B., Series 4697   12 - 15   15 - 18
    E in Ship Sail, Gold Embossed (6)   18 - 22   22 - 25
    EAS, Embossed (6)
    H. CH, Vienne
        Series 123, Lady Chimney Sweep and Pigs   22 - 25   25 - 28
    H & S   12 - 15   15 - 18
    Import, Series 226 (6)
    LP, Series 1371 (6)   15 - 18   18 - 22
    M.S.i.B., Series 13558
    Meissner & Buch
        Series 1545 (6)   18 - 22   22 - 25
        Series 2929 (6) Chimney Sweep Snowmen   22 - 25   25 - 28
    SB
        Series 2226, 2240 Embossed (6) 18 - 22   22 - 25
        Series 2276, Embossed (6)
    Others   12 - 15   15 - 18

CITIES OF THE FUTURE

Miscellaneous   12 - 15   15 - 20
E. J. Schwabe
    "Front St., Port Jervis, N.Y."   15 - 18   18 - 22
    Others, with nice street scenes

CLOWNS

WALL, BERNHARDT (U.S.)
    P. Sander
        "Tom Phoolery, Esq." (Pictured on Cover)   15 - 18   18 - 22
        "You May Fool People ..."
    B. Dondorf
        Series 285 (6) Deco Clowns with hoop   30 - 35   35 - 40
    Raphael Tuck
        Series 117 "At the Carnival" (12) *

City in the Future, E. J. Schwabe
"Front St., Port Jervis, N.Y. ..."

"A Gallant"	18 - 22	22 - 25
"Belle of the Ball"		
"The Cake Walk"	28 - 32	32 - 35
"Confidants"	18 - 22	22 - 25
"Harlequin & Columbine"	22 - 25	25 - 28
"Grace & Beauty"	18 - 22	22 - 25
"Jolly Comrades"		
"La Paloma"		
"Music Hath Charm"		
"Only Teasing"		
"The Queen"		
"Ticklish Situation"		
* Not all cards have Clowns		
Barnum & Bailey Clowns		
Early Poster Types	40 - 50	50 - 60
Color	20 - 25	25 - 30
Real Photos	25 - 30	30 - 40
Anonymous	10 - 15	15 - 20

CUPIDS

SCHMUCKER, S. L. (U.S.) (Uns.)

John Winsch, 1910		
Sports Cupids (4) Valentine		
Fishing Cupid	25 - 30	30 - 35
Football Cupid	30 - 35	35 - 40
Golfing Cupid		

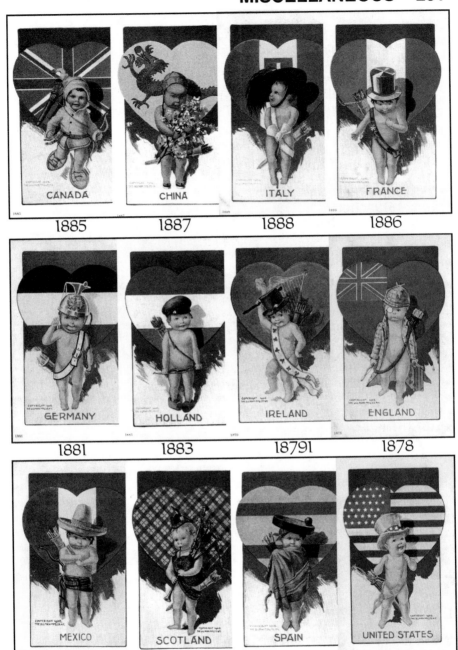

CANADA

CHINA

ITALY

FRANCE

1885   1887   1888   1886

GERMANY

HOLLAND

IRELAND

ENGLAND

1881   1883   18791   1878

MEXICO

SCOTLAND

SPAIN

UNITED STATES

1882   1880   1884   1877

C. H. TWELVETREES
ULLMAN MANUFACTURING CO.
"NATIONAL CUPID" SERIES 76, 1877-1888

Tennis Cupid
Green Heart Cupids (4) Valentine
Irish Lady and Irish Cupid   30 - 35   35 - 40
Oriental lady and Oriental Cupid
Indian Maid and Indian Cupid
Spanish Girl and Spanish Cupid

TWELVETREES, C. H. (U.S.)
   Ullman Mfg. Co.
      "National Cupid" Series 75

1877 "United States"	20 - 25	25 - 30
1878 "England"	15 - 20	20 - 25
1879 "Ireland"		
1880 "Scotland"		
1881 "Germany"		
1882 "Mexico"		
1883 "Holland"		
1884 "Spain"		
1885 "Canada"		
1886 "France"		
1887 "China"		
1888 "Italy"		

WIEDERSEIM, GRACE (U.S.)
   R. Tuck
      Series 200 "Cunning Cupids" (6)
      "For You My Valentine"   40 - 50   50 - 60

PUBLISHERS

ASB	2 - 3	3 - 5
B.W.		
International Art		
Easter Series, S/AB (6)	5 - 6	6 - 8
Trenkler, Germany		
Easter Series with animals (6)	6 - 8	8 - 10
Many other publishers	1 - 2	2 - 4

ANONYMOUS   1 - 2   2 - 4

DEVIL or SATAN

ELLAM, WILLIAM HENRY (G.B.)
   R. Tuck
      "Souvenir" Series 1429
      "New Costume suggested for the ..."   50 - 60   60 - 70
H.
   AMS
      Series 1413
      Devil Spinning Yarn   18 - 22   22 - 25

H., A.M.S. Series 1413
"Spinnata Teifi!" (Spinning Devil)

Anonymous Russian, No. 16
Russian Caption

Ellam, R. Tuck "Souvenir" 1429
"New Costume suggested for ..."

Walt Disney, Czech Issue ca 1930
"Bashful"

Walt Disney, Czech Issue ca 1930
"Grumpy"

LAZOWSKI, A. (Poland)

Polish 37	10 - 12	12 - 15
Anonymous		
Russian	12 - 15	15 - 18
Faust Characters of Satan	12 - 15	15 - 18
Comical; e.g., "Why the Devil don't you write?"	5 - 8	8 - 10

DIABOLO

SHEPHEARD, G. E. (G.B.)

R. Tuck		
"Diabolo" Series		
Santa	30 - 35	35 - 40

THIELE, ARTH. (Germany)

T.S.N.		
Diabolo Series	30 - 35	35 - 38
OTHERS		
Animals	15 - 20	20 - 25
Chicks & Bunnies		

WAIN, LOUIS (G.B.)

R. Tuck		
Series 9563 "Diabolo" (6)		
"Even Baby plays it"	60 - 70	70 - 80
Diabolo - "The Stick Trick"		

DISNEY CHARACTERS (Walt Disney) (U.S.)	20 - 25	25 - 50
Czechoslovakia Issues, 1930's	30 - 35	35 - 60
French issues, 1930's	30 - 40	40 - 75
German issues, 1930's		
Italian issues, 1930's		
Other Foreign, 1930's		
1940's, 1950's issues	12 - 20	20 - 50
"Scenes from Snow White" The Dwarfs		
4227 "Happy"	12 - 15	15 - 20
4228 "Bashful"		
4229 "Doc"		
Others		

DOLLS (See Kewpies, Golliwoggs)

Gartner & Bender		
Rag Doll Series		
"A Wise Guy" (6)	8 - 10	10 - 12
"Amy Bility" (6)		
"Auntie Quate" (6)		
"Dolly Dimple" (6)		
"Epigram" (6)		
"Gee Whiz" (6)		

"Gee Willikins" (6)
"Heeza Korker" (6)
"Jess Cumover" (6)
"Jiminy" (6)
"Optomistic Miss" (6)
"Phil Osopher" (6)

DREAMS

DWIG (Clare Victor Dwiggins) (U.S.)
  R. Tuck

Series 122 "Pipe Dreams" (12)	12 - 15	15 - 18

McCAY, WINSOR (U.S.)
  Raphael Tuck
    Series 6 (12)

"Little Nemo" in Slumberland	25 - 30	30 - 35

"Come Nemo, come, for you I wait..."
"Dear Princess, let the love light..."
"Good morrow, I prith the..."
"I offer you my heart and hand"
Little Nemo on stage.
"The kingdom of thy heart..."
"Princess, if dreams come true..."
"The Princess asks in tender tone..."
"The Princess waits in Slumberland..."
"Thou Princess dost delight..."
"Though Princess, Nemo's far away..."
"To Nemo and the Princess..."

WOLLNER, H. (Germany)

"The Pupil" Dreams of dancing Nudes	18 - 22	22 - 25
Miscellaneous, Many others	5 - 8	8 - 15

DRINKING

DWIG (Clare Victor Dwiggins) (U.S.)
  Raphael Tuck

Series 127 "Toasts for Today" (12)	12 - 15	15 - 20
Series 128 "Toasts for Occasions" (12)		

SCHMUCKER, S. L. (U.S.)
  Detroit Publishing Co., 1907
    "Drink" Series (6)

"Champagne"	125 - 150	150 - 175

"Claret"
"Creme de Menthe"
"Manhattan"
"Martini"
"Sherry"

The "Drink" Series
By
S. L. Schmucker (Unsigned)

Published by Detroit Publishing Company © 1907

"Champagne"

"Claret"

"Creme de Menthe"

"Manhattan"

"Sherry"

"Martini"

Anonymous, Erika 6084
Foreign New Year Greeting

Fritz Baumgarten
Meissner & Buch 3227

EGG PEOPLE, Easter

L.C.R.
    "Colored Egg" People   12 - 15   15 - 20
Others   8 - 10   10 - 15

ELVES

BAUMGARTEN, FRITZ (Germany)
    Meissner & Buch
        3227 New Year Greetings   15 - 18   18 - 22
HARTMAN, EVELYN VON (U.S.)
    E. Nister
        Series 2757 (6) Elves   10 - 12   12 - 15
THIELE, ARTH. (Germany)
    T.S.N.
        Series 928 (6) Christmas Elves   18 - 22   22 - 25

PUBLISHERS
    Erika, Series 6084   12 - 15   15 - 18
    Gottschalk, Dreyfuss & Davis
        Series 2169 (12)   6 - 8   8 - 10
    Others   6 - 8   8 - 10

Real Photo, Martin Post Card Co., ©1909
"The Modern Farmer"

Real Photo by W. H. Martin, ©1909
"How We Catch 'Em in Oklahoma"

E. T. Andrews (Unsigned)
Theo. Stroefer Series 1, Card No. 5063

EXAGGERATIONS

Black & White Types	15 - 20	20 - 25
Real Photo Types		
JOHNSON, A. S. Jr. (U.S.)		
Apples, Peaches, String Beans, Etc.	Range	30 - 100
MARTIN, W. H. (U.S.)		
AZO Photos		
Huge Rabbit, "How We Catch 'Em in ..."	18 - 22	22 - 25
Buick Roadster chasing Jack Rabbit	20 - 25	25 - 30
Auto Hauling Eggs and Potatoes	18 - 22	22 - 25
Giant Fish, Man-eating Fish, Geese	8 - 10	10 - 15
Ducks, Sheep, Poultry, Pigs-Corn		
Grasshoppers, Onions, Watermelons	15 - 18	18 - 22
Watermelons with Blacks	22 - 25	25 - 28
Many Others	15 - 18	18 - 22
Other Photographers	Range	15 - 400
Color and B&W Exaggerations	Range	10 - 50

Note: See Appendix Listing of Book by M. Williams/C. Rubins.

FACES IN BOOTS

Miscellaneous	10 - 15	15 - 20

Anonymous, 150
"Jungfrau"

Anonymous, Series 458
No Caption

Anonymous, Karl Roormagi 129
No Caption

Anonymous, Series 1328
"Eiger, Mönch und Jungfrau"

Unsigned Frances Brundage
Anonymous Series 143

FACES IN CANDLES

Miscellaneous	10 - 12	12 - 15

FACES, FIGURES IN MOUNTAINS

DWIG (Clare Victor Dwiggins) (U.S.)
   Charles Rose

Girls' Figures in Mountains	10 - 12	12 - 15
HANSEN (Germany) Faces in Alps	20 - 30	30 - 50

   Many others
OTHER PUBLISHERS

Chromolithographs	25 - 30	30 - 35
Series 458 (Pictured on Cover)	18 - 22	22 - 25
Others		
Nudes	20 - 25	25 - 30

FLOWER CHILDREN

ANDREWS, E. T. (Unsigned) (G.B.)
   Theo. Stroefer Series 1

5063 Flower Children Series (6)	25 - 30	30 - 35

DULK, M. (U.S.)
   Gibson Art Company
      Birthday, Valentine and General Greetings

Daffodil	15 - 18	18 - 22
Forget-me-not		
Pansy		
Poppy		
Pussy Willow		
Rose (single)		
Red Rose		
Sweet Pea		
Tulip		
Violet		
Wild Rose		
E. Nash		
Series G-53 Months of the Year (12)	25 - 30	30 - 35
Series G-53 Without Months noted (12)	12 - 15	15 - 20

FLOWER FACES

Miscellaneous	6 - 8	8 - 12
BRUNDAGE, FRANCES (U.S.)		
Many early unsigned		
Large close-ups	25 - 28	28 - 32
Small	15 - 18	18 - 22
Others		
CLAPSADDLE, ELLEN (U.S.)	10 - 12	12 - 15
CLAY, JOHN CECIL (U.S.)		
Rotograph Co.		
F.L. 161-172 (12)	35 - 40	40 - 45
Ernest Nister, London	10 - 12	12 - 15
The Standard, London (Multi-Baby)		
Series 67	6 - 8	8 - 10
SCHMUCKER, S. L. (Uns.)		
John Winsch		
Flower Faces Series, Lavender B.G. (6)		
Faces in Tulips	30 - 35	35 - 40
Faces in Easter Lilies		
Faces on red and pink flowers		
Faces on pansies		
Faces in Daffodils		
Faces in pink flowers		
Others, Common	5 - 6	6 - 8
Others, Better	10 - 12	12 - 15
SHINN, COBB 1908 (U.S.)		
E. B. Scofield (Unnumbered Series of 6+)		
Lily	10 - 12	12 - 15
Morning Glory		
Rose		
Tulip		

R. Tuck & Sons' "Garden Truck"
Series No. 2, "A Pretty Pickle!"

G. W. Bonte, Gabriel Series 400
"'Miss Parsnip' said Green ..."

FOOD FANTASY

DWIG (Clare Victor Dwiggins) (U.S.)		
Charles Rose		
"The Wurst Girl" (6)	12 - 15	15 - 18
Miscellaneous	8 - 10	10 - 12

FRUIT & VEGETABLE PEOPLE

WALL, BERNHARDT (U.S.)		
Anonymous (14)		
"You are the APPLE of my eye"	12 - 15	15 - 18
"I'd like to CABBAGE you myself"		
"My love is 22 KARAT fine, dearie"		
"I'm all EARS, tell me about it"		
"I'm cool as a CUCUMBER"		
"I may be a LEMON, but..."		
"I'm your MELON honey"	25 - 30	30 - 35
"I could cry..." Onion	12 - 15	15 - 18
"You and I would make a dandy PAIR"		
"You're the PEACH for me"		
"I'm no Indian, but I do PINE for you"		
"I have my EYES on you" Potato		
"I'm some PUMPKIN"		

H. Schmidt, CKT 1600
Foreign Caption

H. Schmidt, CKT 1601a
Foreign Caption

"I will always TURNIP when you want me"

BONTE, G. W. (G.B.)

    Sam Gabriel Co.

Series 400 (6)		
Apricot-Cucumber "Oh sweet Apricot..."	10 - 12	12 - 15
Celery-Rhubarb "Sweet Celery..."		
Grape-Cucumber "I propose sweet..."		
Potato-Carrot "Oh naughty Potato..."		
Parsnip-Green Pepper "Miss Parsnip..."		
Cauliflower-Green Pea "No word..."		

CURTIS, ELIZABETH (U.S.)

    Raphael Tuck

Series 2 "The Garden Patch"	10 - 12	12 - 15
Series 86 "Garden Patch"		
Apple	10 - 12	12 - 15
Bean		
Beet		
Canteloupe		
Carrot		
Orange		
Peach		
Pear		
Radish		
Red Pepper		
Watermelon		
Other		
Series 87 "Garden Patch" No Border (12)		
Same images as Series 86	8 - 10	10 - 12

SCHMIDT, H. (Germany)

    Carl Kunzle-Tobler

Series 1600		
1600 Carrots and turnips playing cards	25 - 30	30 - 35
1601a Onions playing cards		

THIELE, ARTH. (Germany)

    Carl Kunzle-Tobler

Series 8552 Rutabagas playing cards	25 - 30	30 - 35

GIANT PEOPLE

DWIG (Clare Victor Dwiggins) (U.S.)		
Charles Rose, New York Set (6)	12 - 15	15 - 18
Miscellaneous	5 - 6	6 - 8

GNOMES

BARTH, KATH   (Germany)

Martin Wiegand, Percy Hein 1215
"Der Störenfried" (The Snail)

Kath Barth, R.H. 1196
"Der Philosoph"

Andreas Untersberger, E.K. 1129
"Der Rauchkünstler" (Smoke Artist)

Anonymous, Cellaro
Foreign Caption

THE "GNOME" SERIES
BY
S. L. SCHMUCKER (UNSIGNED)

PUBLISHED BY DETROIT PUBLISHING COMPANY © 1907

1
Humming Bird

2
Bee

3
Mouse

4
Frog

5
Beetle

6
Owl

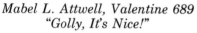

Mabel L. Attwell, Valentine 689
"Golly, It's Nice!"

Signed T.S., Heller's Originals
"Greetings from Folkes"

R.H.
  Series 1196
  "Der Philosoph"   15 - 18   18 - 22

MÜLLER, PAUL L.   (Germany)
  Fingerle & Co.
  326 "Der Mai ist gekommen" May is coming 12 - 15   15 - 18
  Novitas (Oscar Heiermann, Berlin)
    Series 550 "The Lesson of Song"

ROESSLER, A. (Germany)
  Red Head Mushroom Gnomes   15 - 18   18 - 22

SCHMUCKER, S. L. (U.S.)
  "Gnome" Series, Copyright 1907 (6)   200 - 225 225 - 250
    1   Hummingbird
    2   Bee
    3   Mouse
    4   Frog
    5   Beetle
    6   Owl

THIELE, ARTH. (Germany)
  T.S.N. Series 1867 with Snails (6)   20 - 25   25 - 28

UNTERSBERGER, ANDREAS (Germany)
  Emil Kohn, München
    Fairy & Gnome Series (12)
    1126 Dancing   18 - 22   22 - 25

1127 Sewing
1129 "Der Rauchkunstler" - Smoking
Others

WEBER (Germany)	15 - 18	18 - 22

WEIGAND, MARTIN   (Germany)
  T.S.N. (Theo. Stroefer, Nürnberg)

Series 2006		
"Das Bunder"	12 - 15	15 - 18

    "Lieb's Duet"
    "Seben Schwaben"
    Series 2007
    Big Bird
    "Gluchlicher Fang"
    Series 2008
    Hunting
    "King Heinzelman"
    "Nussernte"
    Series 2009
    "Philosopher"
    "Rivalen"
    Series 1218
    "Blumenorakel"
    Other Series
  Percy Hein

Series 1215 (6)		
"Der Storenfried" (The Snail)	15 - 18	18 - 22

WIESBAUER, F.   (Germany)

Gnomes Series	12 - 15	15 - 18

PUBLISHERS

Cellaro	12 - 15	15 - 18

GOLLIWOGGS

ATTWELL, MABEL L. (G.B.)
  Valentine's

Series A551 (6)	18 - 22	22 - 25
Series A579 (6)		
689 "Golly, It's Nice!"	22 - 25	25 - 28

    Series 7346 (6)

GOVEY, A. (G.B)
  Humphrey Milford

"Dreams & Fairies" Series (6)	15 - 18	18 - 22
KENNEDY, T. R. (G.B.)	15 - 20	20 - 25

MARSH-LAMBERT, H.G.C. (G.B.)
  A.M. Davis Co.
    Series 501 "Round the Clock"

"I'll play, I think, with Sambo..."	18 - 22	22 - 25

    "At nine my breakfast is over..."

"Oh Dear! How quickly six has come..."
RICHARDSON, AGNES (G.B)
>   **Raphael Tuck**
>> Series 1232 **"Rescued"** (6)   22 - 25 25 - 28
>> Series 1262, 1281 **"Art"** (6)
>> Series 1397 (6)
>> Card C1420 "Little Snowflakes..."
>> Card C1421 "My Greeting is Loving..." 18 - 22 22 - 25
>> Series C2005   22 - 25 25 - 28
>> Series 8688
>> "I'm down here with the family" 25 - 30 30 - 35
>   **Valentine & Sons**
>> Series C2006 (6)   18 - 22 22 - 25

STOCKS, M. (G.B.)
>   **H.K. & Co.**
>> "Jack-in-the Box" with Golliwogg 15 - 18 18 - 22

UPTON, FLORENCE (G.B.)
>   **Raphael Tuck**
>> **Series 1252**
>> **Series 1281 "Art" Series**
>> "Golliwogg and his Auto-Go-Cart" 35 - 40 40 - 45
>> "Golliwogg taken to Prison"
>> "Golliwogg and his Auto...applying pump"
>> **Series 1282 "Art"**
>>> **Golliwogg w/Dutch Dolls**
>>> "The Golliwogg"   30 - 35 35 - 40
>>> "Golliwogg and the Highwayman"
>>> "Golliwogg Rescued"
>>> "Golliwogg Introducing Himself"
>>> "Golliwogg Taken to Prison"
>>> "Golliwogg Escapes from Prison"
>> **Series 1397** "Humorous" (6) 30 - 35 35 - 40
>> **Series 1782** "New Year" (6)
>> **Series 1785** "New Year" (6) Signed
>> "Golliwogg introduces himself
>> "Highwayman"   35 - 40 40 - 45
>> **Series 1791** (6) Signed
>> Golliwogg and His Auto Car 35 - 40 40 - 45
>> **Series 1792** Christmas, New Year (6) Signed
>> Golliwogg and the Highwayman
>> **Series 1793** (6) Signed
>> Golliwogg in Prison
>> **Series 1794**   (6) Signed
>> **Series 6065** "Humorous" (6)
>> **Series 8063** "New Year" (6)
>   **Davidson Bros. Series**   22 - 25 25 - 30
>   **Regent Publishing Co.**
>   **A. C. Redmon Co.**

Novitas, 52963

Mouton, AVT, Paris

Mouton, AVT, Paris

Mouton, AVT, Paris

Mouton, AVT, Paris

Mouton, AVT, Paris

Plum, AVT 114

Plum, AVT 114

Plum, AVT 114

OTHERS

B.B., London (Birn Bros.) Anonymous Artist

Series 10 Silver Background

Courtship-Marriage w/Stickgirl

At the Beach	20 - 25	25 - 28
In Row Boat		
In Automobile		
On Park Bench		
Playing Cards		
The Family Outing		
Series X296	20 - 22	22 - 25

C. W. Faulkner

Series 996	18 - 22	22 - 25
Series 1136 (6)		

Raphael Tuck

Series 507 (6)	15 - 18	18 - 22
"Art" Series 1262 (6)	15 - 18	18 - 22

John Winsch

1910 Issue	15 - 18	18 - 20
1912 Issue (Santa)	18 - 22	22 - 26
1913 Issue (Santa) (2)	40 - 50	50 - 60

Anonymous

Series 733	15 - 18	18 - 22

HAT FANTASY

PLUM   (France?)

AVT, Paris

Aviator Hat Series 114

Blériot	22 - 25	25 - 28
Curtiss		
Dubonnet		
Latham		
Sommer		
Rougier		
Santos - Dumont		

MOUTON, GEORGES   (France)

AVT, Paris

Big Hat Series (6)	20 - 22	22 - 25

PUBLISHERS

A.R.&C.i.B.

4030 Family with Fruit Hat	12 - 15	15 - 18

B.K.W.I.

Series 307-3 (Signed?)

Novitas

No. 52963 Hippo Lady in Big Hat	20 - 25	25 - 30

Gus Dirks, "Snap-Shots" No. 3
Mrs. Caterpillar: "Why Mr. Beetle, what are you moving for?"

Anonymous, Ludwig Roth 573
The Great Hunter!

Anonymous
Foreign Caption

Willy Schermele, M. Schilling
Foreign Caption

Anonymous
"Fröliche Pfingsten"

R. Kirchner, R. Tuck 2642
"The Mayflies"

Rose O'Neill, Gibson No No.
"Oh, if your chimney ..."

HALEY'S COMET

HESSE
Comics (6)   40 - 50   50 - 75

HEADS IN CLOUDS

KAPLAN
Series 57 Women's heads in clouds (12)   15 - 18   18 - 20
Others   10 - 12   12 - 15

INSECTS

MAY BUGS (MAIKAFIRS, ETC.)

BAUMGARTEN, F. (F.B.) also Uns. (Germany)
Meissner & Buch   Various series   15 - 18   18 - 22
HATZ, H. (Germany)   18 - 22   22 - 25
KIRCHNER, RAPHAEL   (Austria)
R. Tuck
Series 2642 "Mayflies" (6)   200 - 225   225 - 250
OHLER, C.   12 - 15   15 - 18
Others   8 - 10   10 - 12

BUGS, BEETLES, CATERPILLARS, ETC.   10 - 12   12 - 15

DIRKS, GUS (G.B.)
"Snap-Shots" Postcards (8)
3 Mrs. Caterpillar, "Why Mr. Beetle..."   10 - 12   12 - 15
SCHERMELE, WILLY (Germany)
Martin Schilling
"Herzlichen Glückwunsch"   10 - 12   12 - 15

PUBLISHERS

EAS, Series 1144 (6)   15 - 18   18 - 22
Meissner & Buch
M. Munk, Series 1262 (6)   12 - 15   15 - 20
Others   6 - 8   8 - 10

KEWPIES

O'NEILL, ROSE
Campbell Art Co.
"Klever Kards" Folds to form easel-stands up.
Dated 1914 (29)   50 - 55   55 - 60

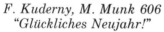

F. Kuderny, M. Munk 606
"Glückliches Neujahr!"

Anonymous, Cellaro
Foreign Caption

Dated 1915 (30+)	55 - 60	60 - 65
Miniature Klever Kards (3 x 4.5)	80 - 90	90 - 100
Suffrage Klever Kard		
228 "Votes for Women-Do I get your Vote?"	150 - 175	175 - 200
Gibson Art Co. (64 in all)	30 - 35	35 - 45
New Years (9)		
Valentine (18)		
Easter (13)		
Christmas (18)		
Miscellaneous types (6)		
Edward Gross Co.		
Large Image Kewpies (6)		
100. "The Kewpie Army"	90 - 100	100 - 120
101. "The Kewpie Carpenter"		
102. "This Kewpie wears overshoes"		
103. "The Kewpie Cook"		
104. "This Kewpie careful of his voice"		
105. "The Kewpie Gardener"		
National Suffrage Pub. Co.		
"Votes for Women - Spirit of '76"	300 - 400	400 - 500
"Votes for our Mothers" (not Kewpies)	450 - 600	600 - 750

OTHERS

Gartner & Bender	8 - 10	10 - 12

S/K.V.
White Kewpies	10 - 12	12 - 15
Black Kewpies	15 - 18	18 - 22

L.P. Co.
White Kewpie-like Children	10 - 12	12 - 15
Black Kewpie-like Children	15 - 18	18 - 22

ANONYMOUS
Series 1067, Birth Announcements (6)	10 - 12	12 - 15
Valentine Series 96	10 - 15	15 - 18

LITTLE MEN-SUPERIOR WOMEN FANTASY

COLLINS
"Little Men" Series	10 - 12	12 - 15

FASCHE, TH. (Germany)
M. Munk, Vienna
"Diabolo" (6)	15 - 18	18 - 22
KYOPINSKI, Little Men (6)	12 - 15	15 - 18

KUDERNY, F. (Austria)
M. Munk, Vienna
Series 606, 699 (6)	12 - 15	15 - 18
Series 556 (6)	15 - 18	18 - 22
N.F., Series 160-165 (6)	10 - 12	12 - 15

MAUZAN, L. (France)
Series 83, Little Men (6)	12 - 15	15 - 18

PENOT, ALBERT (France)
Lapina, Little Men Series (6)	15 - 18	18 - 22

SAGER, XAVIER (France?)
Series 43, Soldiers/Little Women (6)	18 - 20	20 - 25

SCHÖNPFLUG, FRITZ (Austria)
B.K.W.I., Series 4132 (6)	10 - 12	12 - 15

TAM, JEAN (France)
Marque L.E. 70-4	20 - 22	22 - 25

VINCENTINI (Italy)
Deco Ladies in Spider Webs, Little Men	15 - 18	18 - 22

PUBLISHERS

B.G.W.
Series 123/1233 (6)	8 - 10	10 - 12

Bien, Julius, Copyright by J. Marks
Series 155 "Summer Girl" (8)
"A fresh fish every day"	12 - 15	15 - 18

"Everything goes here"
"The game is small but plentiful"
"Nothing like having a pull"
"There is only one safe place..."
"What goes up must come down"

Santway Series 596
Loreley Beckons Boatman

Santway Series 596
Boatman Wrecks on Cliffs

E. Schneider, Moderne Künstler
369, "Loreley"

Carl Gebhardt, E.M.M. 132
"Loreley"

"You never can tell from where you sit"

B.K.W.I.		
Series 136 (6)	8 - 10	10 - 12
L.P.		
Series 105, No. 5 "Ihr Spielzeug"	22 - 25	25 - 28
WBG		
Series 123 (6)	7 - 8	8 - 10

LORELEI, THE SIREN OF THE RHINE

For the millions of tourists who have traveled in Germany, whether by pleasure boat or by train, to see the many beautiful castles on the Rhine, all have heard the legend of The Lorelei (German - Loreley). Above the city of Koblenz, the river swings around a sharp curve at St. Goar, and is forced out of a straight path by a sheer mountain of rock. In the age when river boats were less powerful, strong winds and tricky currents could dash them against this forbidden crag.

Legend turned this terrible rock into either a scaly hideous monster or, even less likely, the echoing bewitching sounds of a beautiful but wicked siren, or river nymph, luring riverboat men to destruction. For this is The Loreley, not a lovely mermaid singing and combing her hair, but simply a mountain of rock. Even today the river barges take extreme care as they travel through the waters and by the precipice, and the excursion boats put on the recorded Loreley song which is sung and played until the danger has passed.

Many beautiful, as well as comical, images were painted of The Loreley, and hundreds of postcards were published from them. One of the most colorful and illustrative 6-card sets, telling the story of the beautiful siren, is Series 596 by Santway, entitled "Die Loreley."

LORELEY

EBERLE, JOSEF (Austria)		
Deutsches Schulverin		
Card 373 Musical praise	18 - 22	22 - 25
Card 1375 Praising her beauty		
GEBHARDT, CARL (Germany)		
E.M.M, Series 132 Nude Loreley	20 - 25	25 - 30
PICHON		
Russian 013, "Lorelei"	12 - 15	15 - 18
RINGS, JOSEF (Germany)		
Edm. von Koenig, Heidelberg		
121 "Die Lorelei"	10 - 12	12 - 15

Anonymous
"Napoleon I"

E.L.D. 33
"Francois Joseph"

Bromura
"Cherchez le viveur"

Anonymous
"Schiller"

SCHNEIDER, E. (Germany)
  Amag Kunst

74 "Loreley" Nude with net	20 - 25	25 - 30

  M.M.B, Moderne Künstler

369 "Loreley" Nude waves net	20 - 25	25 - 30

PUBLISHERS
  Josef Rings, Dusseldorf
    121 "Die Lorelei"
  Santway
    "Die Loreley"
    Series 596 (6)

Beautiful Loreley beckons boatman	22 - 25	25 - 30
Boatman foolishly rows to the cliffs		
Boatman wrecks on the cliffs		
Boatman drowns as Loreley weeps		

  Ottmar Zieher, Munchen

Loreley with harp, boat below at night	12 - 15	15 - 18
Comical "Loreley" with hand mirror		
8721 Loreley with harp, sailboat below		

LOVELY LILLY

FARBER, G. F. (U.S.)
  Fred C. Lounsbury

"Lilly and the Hippopotamus"	40 - 45	45 - 50
"Lily and the Cobra"	40 - 45	45 - 50

MAPS-BODIES MAKING UP COUNTRIES

Early Chromolithos	Range	50 - 100
Collection Des Cent	Range	200 - 250
Miscellaneous	8 - 10	10 - 25

METAMORPHICS (Archiboldesque)

Metamorphics are basically heads of famous people...rulers such as Napoleon, Bismarck, Francis Joseph, Kaiser Wilhelm, Abdul Hamid; the famous composers and musicians...Beethoven, Goethe, Schiller, etc., and comical beings such as Satyr and Unafaune. Most of these heads are either formed completely by nude women (Satyr, Cherchez le viveaux) or are filled with nude women to make the features. Although nudes were the favorite of the artists who painted them, other figures were also used. Horse and horse racing are also used, as are other motifs. The better cards in this group are real photos. The cheaper and poorly printed black and white flat printed issues are not in the same league.

Colombo, GDM 1903-3

PFB, Series 6283

FB (Uns.), M&B 2928

Anon., B. Dondorf 425

PFB, Series 6283

Real Photo

Real Photo

O. Herrfurth, Uva 320

Real Photo, Zena Dare

Publishers Paul Finkenrath of Berlin (**P.F.B.** in Diamond) and **E.D.L.**, Paris did the most beautiful works. However, many nice anonymous copies of almost all issues can also be found. A favorite of many collectors is the nude mermaids forming the face of "Blériot," and that of "Theodore Roosevelt."

GUTMANN, H.
Gutmann & Gutmann
B502 "In most of life we are..."   70 - 75   75 - 85
PUBLISHERS
E.D.L., Paris
26 "Edouard VII"   30 - 35   35 - 40
28 "Alphonse XIII"
33 "Francois Joseph"   40 - 50   50 - 60
62 "Bléroit" Mermaids   50 - 60   60 - 75
Others   30 - 40   40 - 50
Bromura, "Cherchez le viveur"   30 - 35   35 - 40
G.G. Co., "Satyr?"   25 - 30   30 - 35
PFB in Diamond (Real Photos)
Theodore Roosevelt   Range   200 - 250
Series 219
"A Sport"   25 - 30   30 - 35
"Un bon vivant"
"Un faune"
232 "Abdul Kamid"   30 - 35   35 - 40
J. Wollstein, Berlin
"Groeten van Noordwijk" Nudes in Fish   30 - 35   35 - 40
Anonymous *
"A Sport"   25 - 30   30 - 35
"Beethoven"
"Bismarck"
"Diabolo"
"Goethe"
"Graf Zeppelin"   65 - 70   70 - 80
"Liszt"   30 - 35   35 - 40
"Gourmand"
"Horse with Frauen" (Lady Rider)
Jockey and Race Horse
"Kaiser Wilhelm"
"Louvre de Jeunesse, Jungbrunnen"
"Mephisto"
"Napoleon I"
"Napoleon II"
Napoleon - "The Great Conqueror"
"Rossini"
"Schiller"
"J. Strauss"

Anonymous, Erika 5022

I.K., M.P. 4992-1

Anonymous, O.I. 274

Anonymous, E.A.S. 774

Anonymous, BR 7916

Anonymous, P.P. (No No.)

"Un faune"
"Un bon vivant"
"Wagner"
"Xantippe"
Others
* Many are published by **P.F.B., E.D.L.**, etc.

Other Publishers and Anonymous	25 - 30	30 - 35
Black & White issues	8 - 10	10 - 15

MOON (MAN-IN-THE-MOON)

Miscellaneous	8 - 10	10 - 12
BAUMGARTEN, FRITZ Or **F.B.** (Germany)		
Meissner & Buch		
Series 2928 (6) With Children (Uns.)	15 - 18	18 - 22
COLOMBO, E. (Italy)		
G.P.M.		
Series 1903 Deco Dutch Children/Moon (6)	10 - 12	12 - 15
DWIG (Clare Victor Dwiggins) (U.S.)		
Charles Rose		
21 "Moon" Series	10 - 12	12 - 15
HERRFURTH, OSKAR (Germany)		
Uvachrom		
"Die sieben Raben" (with moon)	12 - 15	15 - 18

PUBLISHERS

B. Dondorf, Children in Plane/Moon	12 - 15	15 - 18
P.F.B., Series 6283, Embossed (6)		
Moon with top hat and cane	22 - 25	25 - 28
Moon playing musical instrument		
M. Munk, Vienna		
Series 588 (6) Animals and Moon	15 - 18	18 - 22
Real Photos		
Zena Dare	18 - 22	22 - 25
Man sitting on moon w/U.S. Flag	50 - 75	75 - 100
Others, by photo montage	15 - 25	25 - 50
From studio props	10 - 25	25 - 50

MUSHROOM FANTASY

BARTH, KATH (Germany)		
A.H., with Gnomes		
"Der Philosoph"	12 - 15	15 - 18
BAUMGARTEN, FRITZ or (F.B.) (Germany)		
Meissner & Buch		
Series 1535 (6)	15 - 18	18 - 22

Schutz, B.K.W.I. 557-4
"Schumann: Waldesgesprach"

Schutz, B.K.W.I. 321-6
"Hugo Wolf's Nixe Binse Fuss"

A. P. Lupiac, A.N., Paris 79
"Centaur and Sea-maid"

A. Böcklin, Bruckmanns 2
"The Forest Silence"

AG
    Unsigned **F.B.**   12 - 15   15 - 18
FIALKOWSKA, WALLY   (Austria)
    A.R., **Series 1363**, with Children, Elves (6)   15 - 18   18 - 22
LD
    Meissner & Buch
        Series 2558 (6)   18 - 22   22 - 25
MÜLLER, PAUL L. (Germany)
    "Das Geheimnis"   15 - 18   18 - 22
    "Der Lehrer"
    "Der Zufriedene"
    "Die dre, Mannlein im Waldo Fruhkonzert"
    "Die Lustigen Bruder"
ROESSLER, A. (Germany)   15 - 18   18 - 22
SCHLITT   Elves and Mushroom People   12 - 15   15 - 18
T.K.
    MP, 4992-1   15 - 18   18 - 22
TRUBE, M. (Germany)
    T.S.N. Series 1091, with Children (6)   18 - 22   22 - 25
UNTERSBERGER, ANDREAS (Austria)

PUBLISHERS
    Amag, Series 2238 (6)   15 - 18   18 - 22
    B&R
        Series 7916, with Elves (6)   12 - 15   15 - 18
    Cellaro, Elf Series (6)
    Theo. Eismann, Series 116, Embossed
    Erika
        Series 6084, with Elves (6)   15 - 18   18 - 22
        Series 5022, with Elves
    NW, Series 5-540 (6)   20 - 22   22 - 25
    O.I., Series 274, With Elves
    P.P., with Children   12 - 15   15 - 18
    SYND, With Children
    Anonymous
        Chromolithographs, with Children, Elves   15 - 18   18 - 22
        Others   10 - 12   12 - 15

MUSIC

EBERLE, JOSEF (Austria)
    Deutscher Schulverin - Posters
    373 "Loreley"   18 - 22   22 - 25
    1375 "Loreley"
ELSNER, O. (Austria)
    J. Gestmayer, Wien
        Shubert-Lieder - Poster
        "Der Tod und das Madchen" (Death...)   18 - 22   22 - 25

KUTZER, E. (Austria)
  B.K.W.I.
    Series 628 (6) "Shubert Lieder"
    "Der Wanderer"   12 - 15   15 - 18
    "Erlkonig"
    "Am Meer"
    "Lied Der Mignon"
    Others
SCHUTZ, ERIC (Austria)
  B.K.W.I. Posters
    Series 557 Schumann Music (6)
    1 "Der Nussbaum"   18 - 22   22 - 25
    2 "Im Walde" In the woods
    3 Beautiful Girl with flower blossoms
    4 "Waldesgesprach" Beautiful rider
    "Lotusblume" Nude   25 - 28   28 - 32
    "Venetianscheslied"   15 - 18   18 - 22
    Series 321 Hugo Wolf Music (6)
    4 "Der Gartner"   15 - 18   18 - 22
    5 "Begegrung"
    6 "Nixe Binsefuss" Nude Dancer   28 - 32   32 - 35
    Others
    Series 766 Shubert Music (6)
    3 "Standchen"   12 - 15   15 -20
    4 The Lovers
    5 "Haidenroslein"
    Others
    Series 979 Shubert Music
    5 "Morgengruss" Good Morning   12 - 15   15 - 20

MYTHICAL BEASTS

BÖCKLIN, A. (Germany)
  F. Bruckmann
    2 "The Forest Silence"   15 - 18   18 - 22
    11 "The Centaur at the Smithy"
    20 "Faun and Merl"
    21 "Triton & Nereide" (Merman)
CABANEL, A.
    "Nymphe and Faun"   12 - 15   15 - 20
GEIGER, R. (Hungary)
    Nude, Horse-Beast-Man   18 - 22   22 - 25
HINES, W. (Germany)
  P.F.B. in diamond
    1007 "Rokoko" Nude and Centaur   15 - 18   18 - 22
ISMAILOWITSCH, W. (Germany)
  T.S.N.
    Series 6 "Ein froher Zecher"   15 - 18   18 - 22

LINS, ADOLF (Germany)
  E.A. Schwerdtfeger & Co.

607 "Faun and Nymphe"	12 - 15	15 - 18

LUPIAC, A. P. (France)
  A.N., Paris

79 "Centaur and Sea-maid" (Mermaid)	22 - 25	25 - 30

MICHAELIS, O.
  P.F.B. in diamond

4416 "Centaur and Nymphe"	18 - 22	22 - 25
Others		

WACHSMUTH, M. (Germany)
  P.F.B. in Diamond

"Die Beute"	15 - 18	18 - 22
Others		

RUSSIAN

Real Photo - Nude and Centaur	12 - 15	15 - 18

OTHERS *
  * See Artist S. Schneider in Nude Fantasy Section
PUBLISHERS
  P.F.B. in Diamond

Centaur and Nymphe	15 - 18	18 - 22

ODD-SHAPED PEOPLE

  NVSB

Series 1132 Tall, Skinny People	10 - 15	15 - 20
Others		

PHOTO MONTAGE

IPS 1494 "Chavita"	20 - 25	25 - 30
NPG 464-18 Girl in Bubble	15 - 20	20 - 25
PC 2018-3 Girl in Water		
STP 107-8 "Les Ondines"	12 - 15	15 - 18
Anonymous 405-6 "Fröhliche Ostern"		
Nude Girl in Necktie	Range	175 - 250
Others	Range	15 - 100

PIERROT (Harlequin)

Pierrot was the character in French pantomime who was descended from the Italian mime Pedrolino. Works by French artists usually dressed him in loose fitting pantaloons and white blouse and always with a painted white face. He appeared as an outspoken servant who, at times, would have love affairs with the lady of the house and other scenarios.

Photo Montage, Anonymous 405-6
"Fröhliche Ostern"

Photo Montage
NPG 464-18

Photo Montage
PC 2018/3

Photo Montage, IPS 1494
"Chavita"

Photo Montage, STP 107-8
"Les Ondines"

Anonymous, NVSB Series 1132
Tall, Skinny Couple

ANSCHMIEGENDES WESEN.

Uns. A. Richardson, Cellaro 9918
"Anschmiegendes Wesen"

Italians, especially the great Art Deco artists such as Sofia Chiostri, T. Corbella, Meschini, Scattina, and others, portray him as a reveler and lover of sometime masked beautiful women at parties and clandestine meetings. These works, because of their beautiful and bright colors, have become very collectible in recent years and command relatively high prices as have other Deco renderings.

The English portray the pantomime Pierrot as more of a clown, and some of their ballets represent him as a poet in love with his young and lively sweetheart, Columbine. Americans know him as a "Harlequin," also a character in pantomime who capers and acts like a clown. However, he dresses differently from his European counterparts by wearing a tight-fitting costume covered with diamond shaped patches of bright colors. Regardless of his mode of dress or the part he portrays, he remains a great character in the Fantasy world of postcards.

BAUMGARTEN, FRITZ (Germany)
   Meissner & Buch
      Series 3016 Child Pierrot   22 - 25   25 - 28
BERTIGLIA, A. (Italy)   20 - 25   25 - 30

S. Chiostri
Ballerini & Fratini, Series 244

S. Chiostri
Ballerini & Fratini, Series 212

S. Chiostri
Ballerini & Fratini, Series 197

S. Chiostri
Ballerini & Fratini, Series 224

BUSI, A. (Italy)
  Ross-Monopol   20 - 25   25 - 30
  Degami
    Series 1017   28 - 32   32 - 35
    Series 2074
    Others
CHIOSTRI, S. (Italy)
  Ballerini & Fratini
    Series 117 (4) Children   25 - 30   30 - 35
    Series 178 (4)   30 - 35   35 - 40
    Series 197, 212, 224 (4)   35 - 40   40 - 45
    Series 225 (4) (Uns.)   30 - 35   35 - 40
    Series 228 (4)
    Series 244 (4)   40 - 45   45 - 50
    Series 304 (4) Fairy Series
    Series 305 (4) Mask Series   30 - 35   35 - 40
    Series 357 (4)
    Series 363 (4) Children   25 - 30   30 - 35
    Others
CLIRIO, L. (Italy)   20 - 25   25 - 30
CORBELLA, T. (Italy)
  Degami
    Series 790, 1019   20 - 25   25 - 30
    Series 2087, 3026   25 - 30   30 - 35
    Series 3056 Moon Series   20 - 25   25 - 30
GOBBI, D. (Italy)   25 - 30   30 - 35
MESCHINI, A. (Italy)
  Ars Nova   45 - 50   50 - 60
  STF-Z
    Harlequin Series (Uns.)   40 - 45   45 - 55
    Series 2285
RICCO, LORIS (Italy)   20 - 25   25 - 30
S.K.
    Series 899 Singing Pierrots (6)   18 - 22   22 - 25
S.P.
  Degami
    Series 1035 Spanish Deco   25 - 28   28 - 32
SCATTINA (Italy)   25 - 30   30 - 35
  Sborgi
    "Boheme"
    Sculla Laguna
    Kisses Hand
    "Trice"
    Il Fiore di Pierrot

SMOKING

HUTAF, AUGUST (U.S.)
  Colorgravure

THE "SMOKE" SERIES
BY
S. L. SCHMUCKER (UNSIGNED)
PUBLISHED BY DETROIT PUBLISHING COMPANY © 1907

"Clarice"
Cigarette

"Laughing Waters"
Indian Pipe

"Lucinda"
Cigar

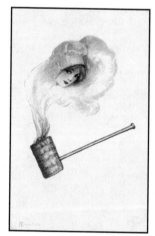

"Maude Miller"
Corncob Pipe

"Molly"
Clay Pipe

"Virginia"
Briar Pipe

Series 138
2302 Human Skull "Still Smoking"   8 - 10   10 - 12
SCHMUCKER, S. L. (U.S.)
   Detroit Publishing Co., 1907
      "Smoke" Series (6) Girl's heads in smoke.
      "Clarice" - Cigarette   125 - 135   135 - 150
      "Laughing Waters" - Indian Pipe
      "Lucinda" - Cigar
      "Maude Miller" - Corncob Pipe
      "Molly" - Clay Pipe
      "Virginia" - Briar Pipe
OTHERS, Heads in Smoke, etc., many   8 - 10   10 - 15

SNAKES

BÖCKLIN, A. (Germany)
   Bruckmanns
      6 "Die Nereide"   15 - 18   18 - 22
SIMONSON-CASTELLI, PROF. (Germany)
      H. Friedrich Abshagen 565 Nude w/snake   18 - 22   22 - 25
DE BOUCHE, A.
   M.K.
      2516 "Salambo"   18 - 22   22 - 25
GADOMSKI, T. (Poland)
      Girl plays harp for snakes   15 - 18   18 - 22
KAPLAN, R. (U.S.)
      Series 56 Male/female snakes entwined
MEUNIER, SUZANNE   (France)
   Marque L-E
      Series 3-26 Nudes and big snakes (6)   35 - 40   40 - 45
RIEHL, JOSEF
      "Laokoon" Snakes   12 - 15   15 - 18
REINACKER, PROF. G.   (Germany)
   Marke J.S.C.
      6082 Partial nude wrapped with snake
   Russian, Anonymous
      752 Nude feeds snake (Real Photo)   12 - 15   15 - 18

SNOWMEN

BAUMGARTEN, FRITZ or (F.B.) (Uns.) (Germany)
   Meissner & Buch
      Series 1845 (6)   22 - 25   25 - 30
      Series 2029 (6)   20 - 25   25 - 28
      Series 2767 (6)   18 - 22   22 - 25
      Series 2929 (6)   25 - 28   28 - 32
      Series 3121 (6)   25 - 28   28 - 32

A. De Bouché, Moderner Kunst
2516, "Salambo"

Prof. G. Rienacker
Marke J.S.C. 6082

Real Photo
Russian Caption

R. Kaplan, Series 56
"Suggestions for Lovers ..."

Series 2856 (6)	15 - 18	18 - 22
"Wintersmann" Series 1845 (6)	28 - 32	32 - 35
Anonymous		
32 Big snowman, hat and scarf (Signed)	25 - 28	28 - 32
Others, signed and unsigned	15 - 18	18 - 22
BUSI, A. (Italy)		
Del Anna & Gasparini		
Series 3059 Women/Snowmen (6)	20 - 25	25 - 28
CASPARI, W. (Germany)	15 - 18	18 - 22
COLOMBO, E. (Italy)		
Series 1887 (6)	15 - 18	18 - 22
EBNER, PAULI		
Early Embossed	22 - 25	25 - 28
M. Munk	18 - 22	22 - 25
B. Dondorf	18 - 22	22 - 25
M. Munk		
Series 694 (6)	22 - 25	25 - 28
FIALKOWSKA, WALLY (Austria)		
Series 1319 (6)	12 - 15	15 - 18
H.J.B.		
Series 114 (6)	8 - 10	10 - 12
HEY, PAUL (Germany)		
Meissner & Buch	12 - 15	15 - 18
J.K.	12 - 15	15 - 18
KUTZER, E. (Austria)	15 - 18	18 - 22
MAILICK, A. (Germany)	18 - 22	22 - 25
PARKINSON, E. (G.B.) Snowman & Children	18 - 22	22 - 25
PEARSE, S. B. (U.S.?)		
M. Munk, Vienna		
Series 879 (6)	20 - 22	22 - 25
ROGIND, CARL (Denmark) (6)	18 - 22	22 - 25
SCHÖNPFLUG, FRITZ (Austria)	15 - 18	18 - 22
THIELE, ARTH. (Germany)		
T.S.N.		
Snowman Series 471 (6)	22 - 25	25 - 28
Snowman Series 1297 (6)		
Snowman Series 1471 (6)		
Others	20 - 22	22 - 25
TRUBE, MAXIM (Germany)	15 - 18	18 - 22
WEBER		
PUBLISHERS		
Amag		
Series 2696, with Animals	12 - 15	15 - 18
B.K.W.I.		
Series 2979 (6)	15 - 18	18 - 22
Cellaro, New Year Snowmen	8 - 10	10 - 12
EAS		
Series 773, with Children	12 - 15	15 - 18

Fritz Baumgarten (Unsigned)
Meissner & Buch, Ser. 1845

F.B. (Fritz Baumgarten)
Meissner & Buch, Series 32

Anonymous, H.W.B. Series 2674
Finnish Caption

F.B. (Unsigned)
Meissner & Buch Series 2929

Erika
Series 6083, with Children (6)   10 - 12   12 - 15
Excelsior
Series 103 (6)   12 - 15   15 - 18
Series 6282 (6)
German-American Novelty Art
Ser. 1036 (6)   10 - 12   12 - 15
H.W.B.
Series 2674, with Elves, Chromolitho   20 - 25   25 - 28
International Art Pub. Co.
Series 2790 (6)   15 - 18   18 - 22
IMPORT
Series 2005 (6)   8 - 10   10 - 12
Meissner & Buch
Series 1845 (6) Hats   15 - 18   18 - 22
P.F.B.
Series 7119, Embossed (6)   15 - 18   18 - 22
P.F.B.
Series 8376, Embossed (6)   18 - 22   22 - 25
Two girls watch boy put hat on snowman
Two girls watch boy put wreath on snowman
Two boys, two girls dance around snowman
Boy, girl standing, boy on snowman
Boy, girl back of fence & boy in front
Other
Series 8378, Embossed (6)   18 - 22   22 - 25
P.P.
Series 8145   10 - 12   12 - 15
S.B.
Series 7226 With children   15 - 18   18 - 22
R. Tuck, Series 274 (6)   15 - 18   18 - 22
V.K., Vienne
Series 5130 (6)   10 - 12   12 - 15
Series 5138 (6)   15 - 18   18 - 22
W.N.
Series 485 Skating Snowmen (6)   15 - 18   18 - 22
Series 569 Comical, with Sun, Moon, Stars
Wezel & Nauman
Series 274, Melting Temperatures (6)   18 - 22   22 - 25

ANONYMOUS

Finnish
Series of 6 large images, with Elves   15 - 18   18 - 22
German
Hold-To-Light (See H-T-L Section)
Series 18, with Children (6)   12 - 15   15 - 18
Series 119, Embossed, with Children (6)   15 - 18   18 - 22

Nanni
Uff. Rev. Stampa 284-1

SB 2891
"Prosit Neujahr!"

Series 183, Embossed, Silver B.G. (6)
Series 547, Embossed, with Children (6)
Series 642, Embossed (6)   15 - 18   18 - 22
German, Embossed New Years   18 - 22   22 - 25

SKYSCRAPERS

DWIG (Clare Victor Dwiggins) (U.S.)
   "New York" Series (6)   12 - 15   15 - 20
Others   8 - 10   10 - 15

SPIDER FANTASY

BUSI, ADOLFO   (Italy)
   Uff. Rev. Stampa
      Series 127-3 Baby & Big Spider   20 - 25   25 - 28
CHIOSTRI, SOFIA   (Italy)
   Ballerini & Fratini
      Series 209 (4) Spider Good Luck Series   35 - 40   40 - 45
NANNI, GIOVANNI   (Italy)
   Uff. Rev. Stampa
      Series 284-1 Lady in the Web   25 - 30   30 - 35

Unsigned Feiertag, B.K.W.I.
685-4 -- No Caption

Anonymous, P.F.B. Series 6289
No Caption

PUBLISHERS
    SB, Series 2891 Ugly Woman in Web   15 - 18   18 - 22
Others, many   8 - 10   10 - 15

STICK OR WOOD PEOPLE

    Miscellaneous (See Golliwoggs)   10 - 12   12 - 15

STORKS

GASSAWAY, KATHERINE (U.S.)
    Raphael Tuck
        Series 2495 "The New Baby" (6)
        "Hello, are you there..."   8 - 10   10 - 12
        "Just arrived by stork express..."
        "Mr. Stork, the Universal Provider"
        Others
FEIERTAG, KARL (Unsigned) (Austria)
    B.K.W.I. 685-4   12 - 15   15 - 20

PUBLISHERS
    E. Nash
        Series 1 (6)   8 - 10   10 - 15

Series 2 (6)
P.F.B.

Series 3672, 5511, 6289, 7906 (6) Emb.	12 - 15	15 - 18
Series 8772, 9532 (6) Birth Announcements		
Roth & Langley Comics	6 - 8	8 - 10
Winsch, John © 1910, 1911 (6)	12 - 15	15 - 18
A. Selige No Number Series (6)	6 - 8	8 - 10
R. Tuck Series 2768 (6)	8 - 10	10 - 12
Other publishers	6 - 8	8 - 10

SUNBONNETS

CORBETT, BERTHA (U.S.)
J. I. Austen

"Days of the Week" 258-264 (7)		
Monday	10 - 12	12 - 15
Tuesday		
Wednesday		
Thursday		
Friday		
Saturday		
Sunday		
Series 119 -124 (Uns.)	10 - 12	12 - 15
Beckwith Series	12 - 15	15 - 18

DIXON, DOROTHY (U.S.)
Ullman Mfg. Co.

Sunbonnets 503-512 (10)	10 - 12	12 - 15
Sunbonnet Girls 1385-1390		

WALL, BERNHARDT (U.S.)
S. Bergman

T. P. Co. (Taylor-Platt)	10 - 12	12 - 15

Ullman Mfg. Co.

"Days of the Week" (Uns.)		
1408 "Wednesday" Mending	12 - 15	15 - 18
1409 "Monday" Washing Clothes		
1410 "Tuesday" Ironing		
1491 "Thursday" Baking		
1492 "Friday" Cleaning		
1493 "Saturday" Marketing		
1494 "Sunday" Going to Church		
"Months of the Year" (12) (Uns.)		
1633 "January"	12 - 15	15 - 18
1634 "February"		
1635 "March"		
1636 "April"		
1637 "May"		
1638 "June"		
1639 "July"		

Sunday, 1494

Monday, 1409

Tuesday, 1410

Wednesday, 1408

Thursday, 1491

Friday, 1492

Saturday, 1493

SUNBONNET DAYS OF THE WEEK
Ullman Mfg. Company © 1905
By Bernhardt Wall (Unsigned)

Sunday:	*Church Day*
Monday:	*Wash Day*
Tuesday:	*Ironing Day*
Wednesday:	*Mending Day*
Thursday:	*Baking Day*
Friday:	*Cleaning Day*
Saturday:	*Market Day*

1640 "August"		
1641 "September"		
1642 "October"		
1643 "November"		
1644 "December"		

"Mottos" With 2 girls

1645 "Give us this day our daily bread"	10 - 12	12 - 15
1646 "The Star Spangled Banner..."	12 - 15	15 - 18
1647 "Should auld acquaintance be forgot"	10 - 12	12 - 15
1648 "A good book is the best companion"		
1649 "Now I lay me down to sleep..."		
1650 "Be it ever so humble..."		

"Seasons" (4)

1901 "Spring"	10 - 12	12 - 15
1902 "Summer"		
1903 "Autumn"		
1904 "Winter"		

"The Sunbonnet Twins" (6)

1645 "Give us this day our daily bread" *	10 - 12	12 - 15
1646 "The Star Spangled Banner"		
1647 "Should auld acquaintance be forgot?"		
1648 "A good book is the best companion"		
1649 "Now I lay me down to sleep..." *		
1650 "Be it ever so humble..."		

* Unsigned

"Nursery Rhymes" (Uns.) (6) - See Nursery Rhymes

1664 "Little Bo Peep..."	15 - 18	18 - 22
1665 "To Market, to market..."		
1666 "Rain, rain go away..."		
1667 "See saw, Marjorie Daw..."		
1668 "Goosey, Goosey, Gander..."		
1669 "Come, let's go to bed..."		

"Mary and Her Lamb" Sunbonnets (4)

1759 "Mary had a little lamb..."	15 - 18	18 - 22
1760 "Everywhere that Mary went..." *		
1761 "It followed her to school one day..." *		
1762 "It made the children laugh..." *		

* Unsigned

"Hours of the Day"

1765 "6 A.M., Milking Time"	10 - 12	12 - 15
1766 "7 A.M., Breakfast Time"		
1767 "10 A.M., Mowing Time"		
1768 "12 Noon, Noon Time"		
1769 "3 P.M., Haying Time"		
1770 "6 P.M., Home, Sweet Home"		

ANONYMOUS

Bergman Co.

"Dear Friend, Greeting..."	8 - 10	10 - 12

Real Photo, Maquette de Giris, A-N, Paris
"W. Wright" -- "Un vol á l'americaine"

Real Photo, Giris, A-N, Paris
"W. Wright" -- "Diseau Trans..."

Aéro-Taxi dans 20 ans
"Chocolat Lombart," Paris

"Luv"
H. I. Robbins, Boston, 1907
Series 897, Emb. (7)
    897-7 Sunday - Twins going to Church   12 - 15   15 - 18
Advertising
    Majestic Range Adv. Series   18 - 22   22 - 25

TRANSPORTATION

BEM, E. (Russia)
  Lapina
    82 Russian, Porcupine transportation   20 - 25   25 - 30
  Rishar
    58 Russian, Balloon transportation
BRUNDAGE, FRANCES (U.S.)
  Anonymous
    Stick Horse transportation   20 - 22   22 - 25
    Flower Boat transportation   15 - 18   18 - 22
    Flower bouquet, with Cupids pulling   12 - 15   15 - 18
  Others
CLAPSADDLE, ELLEN (U.S.)
  International Art
    Various Series Flower Autos, etc.   8 - 10   10 - 12
    Air Zeppelins, Balloons, etc.
  Others
H.B.G. (H.B. GRIGGS) (U.S.)
  L. & E.
    Series 2254 (6)
    Egg and bunny transportation   12 - 15   15 - 18
GIRIS, C. (France)
  A-N, Paris (Real Photos)
    Aviation Series
    "W. Wright" "Diseau Transatlantique"   50 - 60   60 - 75
    "W. Wright" "Un vol a l'Americaine"
MOUTON, G. (France)
  Anonymous Comical Aviator Series
    "Le Wright"   25 - 28   28 - 32
PENOT, ALBERT (France)
  Paris Salon Teal Photo types
    2093 Glamourous Nude Witch riding broom   25 - 28   28 - 32
PONG
    Baby Bottle transportation   10 - 12   12 - 15
R.K. (Austria)
  B.K.W.I.
    Series 3165 (6) Pig carts, Dog carts, etc.   12 - 15   15 - 18
SANDFORD, H. D. (G.B.)
  R. Tuck
  Happy Little Coons Series 9457

E. Bem, Rishar 58
Balloon Transportation

Feder und Tinte bring' ich Dir . . . – – Nun schreibe mir!!

Unsigned, S.W.S.B. 9658
Ink and Pen Transportation

Pong, Anonymous
"Look! Before You Leap"

S. Chiostri, Ballerini & Fratini
347, Dragonfly Transportation

Unsigned, R. Tuck "Aeroplanes"
Series 9935, "Latham's" Aeroplane

E. Bem, Lapina 82
Porcupine Transportation

Unsigned, P.P.
The Pig Flying Machine

"The Camel Race" - Camel   15 - 18   18 - 22
"Hold Tight" - Alligator
"A Friend in Need"
"A trip on the Briny" Turtle
ZAHL, H. (Germany)
  A.R. & C.i.B
    825-20 "Little Witch" Nude riding broom   25 - 30   30 - 35

PUBLISHERS

B.K.W.I.
  Series 4106 (6) Blacks
    Black jockey rides rooster   22 - 25   25 - 28
    Black driver in egg wagon pulled by chicks
S.W.S.B.
  9658 Ink and Ink pen series   12 - 15   15 - 20
R. Tuck
  "Aeroplanes" Series 9936 (6)
  People of weight on "Latham's" Aeroplane.   30 - 35   35 - 38
  A hunting we go on "Farman" Aeroplane.
  Hold tight on the "Wright" Aeroplane.
  Making History on the "Bléroit" Aeroplane.
  Series 10 "Love Missives"
Dragonfly transportation   10 - 12   12 - 15

MISCELLANEOUS

Airships (Balloons, Zeppelins, Airplanes)   10 - 12   12 - 20
  People in real autos over cities   12 - 15   15 - 18
  Named cities   18 - 22   22 - 25
  Dragonflies   10 - 12   12 - 15
  Egg Auto, Bus, or Coach
  Flying Carpets
  Grasshoppers
  Pigs
  Studio posed for people in autos, planes, etc.   10 - 15   15 - 20
ADVERTISING
  Chocolat Lombart
    Aero-Taxi   20 - 25   25 - 30

WILD ANIMALS/LADIES FANTASY

BEROUD, L. (France)
  S.I.P., Series 20 "Fantaisie"   15 - 20   20 - 25
CHIOSTRI, SOFIA (Italy)
  Ballerini & Fratini, Series 320 (4)   40 - 45   45 - 48
CORBELLA, T. (Italy)
  Degami
    Series 636 (6)   20 - 25   25 - 28

A. Zandrino, Uff. Rev. Stampa
18-4

S. Chiostri, Ballerine & Fratini
320

A. Zandrino, Uff. Rev. Stampa
18-3

A. Guerzoni, Proprieta Artistica
480-5

T. Corbella, Degami
636

L. Beroud, S.I.P. 20
"Fantaisie"

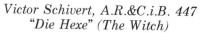

Victor Schivert, A.R.&C.i.B. 447
"Die Hexe" (The Witch)

B.D., Axel Eliassons Konstförlag
No. 6476, "Glad Pask"

GUERZONI, G.   (Italy)
   Proprieta Artistica, Series 480 (6)   15 - 20   20 - 25
ZANDRINO, A. (Italy)
   Uff. Rev. Stampa
      Series 18 (6)   25 - 28   28 - 32
Others   10 - 15   15 - 20

WITCHES

FROMME, L.   (Germany)
   Witch and Elves   15 - 18   18 - 20
HENDRICH, HERMAN (Germany)
   Meisenbach Riffarth & Co.
      20961 "Hexenfahrt"   12 - 15   15 - 18
HIRSCH   (Germany)
   "Walpurgisnacht" (Nude Witches)   18 - 25   25 - 50
LINGER (Germany)
   "Die Hexe" The Witch handcuffed   15 - 18   18 - 22
MAILICK, A. (Germany)
   C. Bruning, Brocken
      "Gruss vom Brocken" Nude Witch   25 - 35   35 - 50
MOUTON, G. (France)
   A.N., Paris
      Glamourous witch rides broom   25 - 28   28 - 32

Otto Stieffel, Edm. v. König
Card 4, "Hexleins erste Fahrt"

Otto Stieffel, Edm. v. König
Card 10, "Hule"

H. Zahl, A.R.&C.i.B. Series 825
"Little Witch"

A Penot, J.K. 2093
"Dé Part Pour Le Sabbat"

PENOT, A. (France)
    J.K.

2093, Paris Salon "Dé Part Pour Le Sabbat"	22 - 25	25 - 28

SOLOMKO, S. (Russia)
    T.S.N.

94 "Fortune-Telling" Witch & Owl	15 - 18	18 - 22

VOGEL

Children and Witch	15 - 18	18 - 22

ZAHL, H. (Germany)
    AR. & C.i.B.

Series 825-20 "Little Witch" Nude	25 - 30	30 - 35
(Note: Pictured on Cover)		

OTHERS

	10 - 15	15 - 20

WITCHES, EASTER (Scandinavia) **

A.S. (Sweden) (1910-1920)	15 - 18	18 - 22
B.D. (Sweden) "Glad Pask"	20 - 22	22 - 25
ALANEN, JOSEPH (Finland) (Pre 1920)	12 - 15	15 - 18
BROLIN, GUNNEL (Finland) (1940's)	6 - 8	8 - 10
HEIDE, ANNE-MARIE (Finland) (1930's)	8 - 10	10 - 12
CLEMENT, GUNAR (Finland) (1920's)	12 - 15	15 - 18
DORPH, INGRID (Finland) (1940's)	8 - 10	10 - 12
E.L. (Sweden) (1930's)	6 - 8	8 - 10
E.S.T. (Sweden) (1930's)	8 - 10	10 - 12
FAGERHOLM, INGA (Finland) (1940's)	8 - 10	10 - 12
K-LINDHOLM, DORIS (Finland) (1940's)	6 - 8	8 - 10
KLEIN, I. (Sweden) (1930's)	8 - 10	10 - 12
SJOSTEDT, HELGA (Finland) (1930's)	6 - 8	8 - 10
STEENHOFF, SIGRUN (Sweden) (1910-1920)	12 - 15	15 - 18
STOOPENDAAL, G. (Sweden) (1910-1920)	12 - 15	15 - 18
TELEGIN, M. (M. Trigg) (Finland) (1940')	6 - 8	8 - 10
TILGMANN, ARNOLD (Finland) (1940's)	8 - 10	10 - 12
VIKSTEDT, KARIN (Finland) (1930's)	8 - 10	10 - 12

  ** Add $5 to $8 for images on Miniature Cards.

PUBLISHERS
    Louis Glaser, Leipzig

Grus aus dem Harz	15 - 18	18 - 22
M.J.S., Series 104 "Die Hexe"	15 - 18	18 - 22

    Ernest Thill, Bruxelles

"The young sorceress" (B&W)	12 - 15	15 - 18

ANONYMOUS

426 Witch flies out of chimney	20 - 25	25 - 28
"Gruss vom Brocken" Devil & Nude Witches	20 - 30	30 - 40
Other Brocken cards	15 - 18	18 - 35

OTHER MISCELLANEOUS
WIENER WERKSTAETTE ARTISTS: There were many fantasy cards by the WW artists. They range in price from $150 to $1000 each, depending on the specific artist and image.

Appendix

POSTCARD PUBLISHERS & DISTRIBUTORS

Following are some of the major publishers of postcards world-wide. Minor publishers can be found under each particular listing throughout this book.

AMAG — Artist-Signed, Fantasy
A.M.B. — Meissner & Buch, Quality Greetings, Artist-Signed
A.S.B. — Greetings
Ackerman — Pioneer Views of New York City
Albertype Co. — Pioneer & Expo Views; Local Views
Am. Colortype Co. — Expositions
Am. News Co. — Local Views
Am. Post Card Co. — Comics
Am. Souvenir Co. — Pioneers
Anglo-Am. P.C. Co. (AA) — Greetings, Comics
Art Lithograph Co. — Local Views
Asheville P.C. Co. — Local Views, Comics
Auburn P.C. Mfg. Co. — Greetings, Comics
Austin, J. — Comics
Ballerini & Fratini, Italy — Chiostri, Art Deco
BKWI, German — Artist-Signed, Comics
Bamforth Co. — Comics, Song Cards
Barton and Spooner — Comics, Greetings
Bergman Co. — Comics, Artist-Signed Ladies, etc.
Julius Bien — Comics, Greetings, etc.
B.B. (Birn Brothers) — Greetings, Comics
Bosselman, A.C. — Local Views, Others
Britton & Rey — Expositions, Battleships, etc.
Brooklyn P.C. Co. — Views
Campbell Art Co. — Comics Rose O'Neill, etc.
Chapman Co. — Greetings, College Girls, etc.

Charlton, E.P. — Expositions, Local Views
Chisholm Bros. — Expositions, Local Views
Colonial Art Pub. Co. -- Scenics, Comics, Sepia Lovers
Conwell, L.R. — Greetings
Crocker, H.S. — Local Views
Davidson Bros. — Greetings, Artist-Signed
Dell Anna & Gasparini, Italy — Art Deco
Delta, Paris — French Fashion
Detroit Pub. Co. — Prolific Publisher, All Types
Faulkner, C.W., British — Artist-Signed, Greetings
Finkenrath, Paul, Berlin (PFB) — Greetings
Gabriel, Sam — Greetings
German-American Novelty Art — Greetings, Comics
Gibson Art Co. — Comics, Greetings
Gottschalk, Dreyfus & Davis — Greetings
Gross, Edward — Artist-Signed
Hammon, V.O. — Local Views
Henderson & Sons — Artist-Signed, Comics
Henderson Litho — Greetings, Comics, Local Views
S. Hildesheimer — Artist-Signed, Comics, Fantasy
Huld, Franz — Installment Sets, Expositions, etc.
Ill. Postal Card Co. — Greetings, Artist-Signed and Many Others
Int. Art Publishing Co. — Greetings by Clapsaddle, etc.
Knapp Co. — Artist-Signed
Koeber, Paul C. (P.C.K.) — Comics, Artist-Signed
Koehler, Joseph — H-T-L, Expositions, Local Views
Kropp, E.C. — Local Views, Battleships, etc.
Langsdorf, S. — Alligator and Shell Border Views, Local Views, Greetings
Lapina, Paris — Color Nudes and French Fashion
Leighton, Hugh — Local Views
Leubrie & Elkus (L.&E.) — Artist-Signed
Livingston, Arthur — Pioneers, Local Views
Lounsbury, Fred — Greetings, Local Views, etc.
Manhattan P.C. Co. — Local Views, Comics
Vivian Mansell & Co. — Artist-Signed
Marque L-E, Paris — French Fashion
Meissner & Buch, German — Artist-Signed, Greetings
Metropolitan News Co. — Local Views
Mitchell, Edward H. — Expositions, Battleships, Local Views
Munk, M., Vienna — Artist-Signed, Comics, etc.
Nash, E. — Greetings
National Art Co. — Artist-Signed, Greetings, etc.
Nister, E., British — Artist-Signed, Greetings
Novitas, Germany — Artist-Signed
Noyer, A., Paris — Nudes and French Fashion
O.P.F. -- Quality German Artist-Signed
Oppel & Hess — Artist-Signed, Fantasy
Owen, F.A. — Greetings, Artist-Signed
Phillipp & Kramer, Vienna — Artist-Signed, Art Nouveau
Platinachrome — Artist-Signed, Earl Christy, etc.
Reichner Bros. — Local Views
Reinthal & Newman — Artist-Signed, Greetings
Rieder, M. — Local Views
Rose, Charles — Greetings, Song Cards, Artist-Signed, Comics

Rost, H.A. — Pioneer Views, Battleships
Roth & Langley — Greetings, Comics
Rotograph Co. — Local Views, Expostiions, Battleships, Artist-Signed, etc.
Sander, P. — Greetings, Comics, Artist-Signed
Santway — Greetings
Sborgi, E., Italy — Famous Art Reproductions
Selige, A. — Expositions, Western Views, People, etc.
Sheehan, M.T. — Local Views, Historical, Artist-Signed
Souvenir Post Card Co. — Local Views, Greetings, etc.
Stecher Litho Co. — Greetings, Artist-Signed
Stengel & Co., Germany — Famous Art Reproductions
Stewart & Woolf, British — Comics, Artist-Signed
Stokes, F.A. — Artist-Signed, Comics
Strauss, Arthur — Local Views, Historical, Expositions
Stroefer, Theo. (T.S.N.), Nürnburg — Artist-Signed, Animals, etc.
Taggart Co. — Greetings
Tammen, H.H. — Expositions, Historical, Local Views
Teich, Curt — Local Views, Artist-Signed, Comics
Tichnor Bros. — Later Local Views, Comics
Tuck, Raphael & Sons, British — Artist-Signed, Views, Comics, Greetings, etc.
Ullman Mfg. Co. — Greetings, Artist-Signed, Comics
Valentine & Sons, British — Artist-Signed, Comics, Views, etc.
Volland Co. — Artist-Signed, Greetings
Whitney & Co. — Greetings, Artist-Signed
Winsch, John — Greetings, Artist-Signed
Wirths, Walter — Pioneer Views

BIBLIOGRAPHY

The following publications, all related to the collection and study of postcards, are recommended for further reading.

All About Dwig, Bonnie P. Miller, Palm Bay, FL, 1976

American Advertising Postcards, Sets and Series, 1890-1920, Fred and Mary Megson, Martinsville, NJ, 1987

The American Postcard Guide to Tuck, Sally Carver, Brookline, MA, 1979

The American Postcard Journal, Roy and Marilyn Nuhn, New Haven, CT

The Artist-Signed Postcard Price Guide, J. L. Mashburn, Colonial House

Art Nouveau Post Cards, Alan Weill, Image Graphics, NY, 1977

Bessie Pease Gutmann, Published Work s Catalog, Victor J.W. Christie, Park Avenue Publishers, NJ, 1986

The Collector's Guide to Post Cards, Jane Wood, Gas City, IN

A Directory of Postcard Artists, Publishers and Trademarks, Barbara Andrews, 1975

Encyclopedia of Antique Postcards, Susan Nicholson, Wallace-Homestead, 1994

Larger Than Life: The American Tall-Tale Postcard 1905-1915. Exaggeration Real Photo Postcards, Morgan Williams and Cynthia Rubins

Guide to Artists' Signatures & Monograms on Postcards, Nouhad A. Saleh., 1993 Minerva Press, Boca Raton, FL 33429-0969, USA

Halloween Postcards Published by John Winsch, Hazel Leler, Houston, 1994

Neudin Cartes Postales de Collection, 1991, 35 rue G. St-Hilaire, 75005 Paris

Official Postcard Price Guide, Dianne Allman, House of Collectibles, NY, 1990

Philip Boileau, Painter of Fair Women, D. Ryan, Gotham Book Mart, NY, 1981

The Postcard Catalogue, 1993, Venman, Smith, Mead, IPM, U.K.

Picture Postcards in the U.S., 1893-1918, Dorothy Ryan

Picture Postcards of the Golden Age, Tonie & Valmai Holt, U.K.

Prairie Fires & Paper Moons: The American Photographic Postcard, 1902-1920, Hal Morgan, Andreas Brown, Boston, 1981

Real Photo Postcards, Robert Ward, Bellevue, 1994

The Postcard Price Guide, 2nd Ed., J.L. Mashburn, Colonial House, Enka, NC

The Postcards of Alphonse Mucha, Q. David Bowers, Mary Martin

Standard Postcard Catalog, 1982, James L. Lowe, PA

The Super Rare Postcards of Harrison Fisher, J. L. Mashburn, Enka, NC, Colonial House

Vintage View of Christmas Past, Jim Morrison, York, PA, 1995

What Cheer News, Mrs. E.K. Austin, Editor, Rhode Island Postcard Club, RI

PERIODICALS

The Antique Trader Weekly, P.O. Box 1050, Dubuque, IA 52004

Antiques & Auction News, P.O. Box 500, Mt. Joy, PA 17552

Barr's Post Card News, 70 S. 6th St., Lansing, IA 52151

Collector News & Antique Reporter, P.O. Box 156, Grundy Center, IA 50638

New England Antiques Journal, 4 Church St., Ware, MA 01082

Paper Collectors Marketplace, P.O. Box 127, Scandinavia, WI 54977

Paper Pile Quarterly, P.O. Box 337, San Anselmo, CA 94979

Picture Post Card Monthly, 15 Debdale Ln, Keyworth, Nottingham NG12 5HT, U.K.

The Postcard Album, H. Luers, Anton-Gunther-Str. 12, W-2902, Rastede, Germany

Postcard Collector, P.O. Box 1050, Dubuque, IA 52004

MAJOR POSTCARD AUCTION HOUSES

Antique Paper Guild, P.O. Box 5742, Belleview, WA 98006 Real Photo Specialists

Bennett's, Pickering Road, Dover, NH 03820

Butterfield & Butterfield, 220 San Bruno Ave., San Francisco, CA 90046

The First National Postcard Auctions, P.O. Box 5398, Hamden, CT 06518

Swann Galleries, Inc., 104 East 25th St., New York, NY 10010

Index

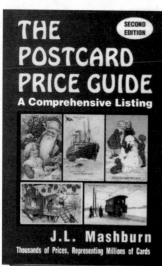
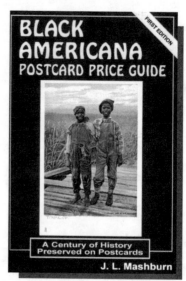